Listen to the Locals

Wise up to the weather

Margaret Dye

Larks Press

Published by the Larks Press
Ordnance Farmhouse, Guist Bottom,
Dereham NR20 5PF

01328 829207

Printed by the Lanceni Press
Garrood Drive, Fakenham

Published June 2002, Reprinted June 2003

British Library Cataloguing-in-Publication-Data
A catalogue record for this book is available from the British Library

The author and publisher wish to thank all those who have lent
photographs for this book. The photograph on page 44 is by Stephen Pond.

Front cover: Anthony Jordan against a photo by Frank Dye

ISBN 1 904006 07 8

Contents

Introduction

Weather forecasting probably began with the shamans and witch doctors of early civilisations who, from observation of the natural world, may have tried to forecast weather patterns, so essential to the survival of farmers and hunters. Certainly, as early as 900 BC, the Greeks kept rainfall records.

In 1892 the publication *A Collection for the Improvement of Husbandry and Trade* printed weather readings for the same week of the previous year in an effort to predict weather.

The first media weather forecast was on January 3rd 1921 from the University of Wisconsin radio station. Now, in the 21st century, the University of East Anglia's world-famous department of Environmental Sciences and the Tyndall Centre for Research into Climate Change produce studies on this subject for all the world to read. The *Eastern Daily Press* for February 10th 2001 reported from these sources that warmer weather might result in outbreaks of malaria in the marshes of North Norfolk and the Broads in the future. The report, the first of its kind in Europe, also warns that by 2050 rising temperatures may result in extra heat-related deaths and 5000 more cases of skin cancer each year. Average temperatures in the UK are expected to rise by up to 2.3 degrees centigrade, with the country experiencing hotter drier summers and more intense heat waves. Winters are expected to get warmer and wetter. News media relay to the world the dreadful climatic disasters to humans, droughts, floods, earthquakes, cyclones, hurricanes, heat waves, forest fires and food-crop failures with many millions of deaths resulting in many parts of the world.

The world's climate has been warming for the past eighty years at least. As a result, sea water is expanding, ice caps and glaciers melting and, as a consequence, sea levels are rising. Levels of polluting gases, carbon dioxide, methane and nitrous oxides, thought to be the cause of the 'Greenhouse Effect', are increasing. Power stations using fossil fuels produce carbon dioxide as does burning countryside waste products; forests produce carbon dioxide, farmyard animals make methane and an increasing army of motor vehicles spew out carbon dioxide and nitrous oxides. The polluting gases trap heat, and as the earth gets warmer, more sea water will evaporate to make more clouds. Clouds block heat escaping from the earth; clouds are also getting thicker due to sulphur pollution.

Indeed, even as this book is being prepared, the Country File television programme on BBC1 (Feb 24th 2001) has devoted its entire programme to climate change, asking the viewers to observe and record changing patterns of plant and animal behaviour. The programme claims that snowdrops, daffodils, bluebells and hawthorn (a good climate indicator) are all coming into flower at least one month earlier than fifty years ago. The Woodland Trust have records dating back to the early 17th century. In the past, they have used their power to protect the environment from urbanisation, but in the future, they will need to enlarge their concerns as climate change may cause disruption to the ecological balance of plant and animal species.

Climate change appears to be inevitable, but by listening to the locals, whether they live and work in 2002 or 3002, we may stay in touch with our weather. In this increasingly urbanised society world weather may be accessed at the touch of a mouse, yet to live life to the full we need to read weather signs around us so that we can enjoy planet earth and help to look after it for future generations. Climate is a long-term look at weather.

In January 2001 it was officially accepted that man's intervention on our planet is partly responsible for global warming, and the 'greenhouse effect'. If unchecked, this climate change will drastically affect the world's forests and wildlife. Alterations to world forests and rising ocean levels, shifting rainfall patterns and increasingly frequent and violent tropical storms, may well disrupt life all over planet earth.

Damage to the ozone layer in this industrial age is causing chloro-fluoro-carbons to be released into earth's atmosphere. Higher concentrations of carbon dioxide, methane, and other gases are trapping the solar heat. The first discovery of pollution attacking the ozone layer, which protects the earth from the harmful rays of the sun, was made in the Antarctic in 1982. Four years later, a hole in the ozone layer was recorded over the Arctic.

More violent and unpredictable weather may be on its way. Predicting weather in the future may therefore become more difficult, yet observant amateurs, especially farmers and fishermen, who owe not only their livelihoods, but also their lives to 'getting it right', can teach the rest of us a great deal about weather watching. Today, those of us who enjoy active leisure activities such as gardening, walking, climbing, hang-gliding, sailing or fishing, or just want to know

5

whether it is safe to hang the washing outside before going to work, may learn to make reasonably accurate short-term forecasts by learning to be observant.

Sea ice off Brancaster Staithe in 1963
Hard winters like this may be rarer in future

What is weather?

The earth is surrounded by a blanket of air or **atmosphere**; this is a mixture of water vapour and gases. Weather can be a term used to describe a variation in our day to day atmosphere.

The weather we experience locally depends on three ingredients, in a variety of mixtures: **heat** from the sun, **wind** (air in motion), and **water** on the air in the form of gas (water vapour) or water droplets.

Meteorologists record temperature with thermometers, wind speed and direction with an anemometer; rainfall is measured with a rain gauge and atmospheric pressure with a barometer. This pressure is best described as the weight of air on the earth's surface; a rising barometer indicates the approach of a high pressure system when good weather will be enjoyed; a falling barometer indicates the arrival of a low pressure system when poor weather may be expected. Cloud-cover and humidity are also accounted for as weather forecasters prepare their reports, using satellite pictures, charts and computer models, laced with experience and understanding of the highs and lows as the weather systems track across our planet.

Weather, in the northern latitudes, generally travels from west to east.

Generally winds from the north or north-west bring in warm air. East winds are usually caused by a counter-clockwise rotation of a low pressure centre, and when west winds predominate they indicate stable weather. Changes in wind direction is an important clue when weather watching.

Sea breezes, especially in late spring and summer are the result of the land warming during the day faster than the sea; therefore air over the land warms and rises, whilst cooler air over the sea is drawn in to take its place.

Land breezes happen at nights when the land loses its heat more quickly than over the water masses. Therefore warmer air over the water rises and is replaced by cooler air blown from the shore.

Mountain winds are also the result of temperature changes. Valley breezes occur during the daytime. Mountains heat up more quickly than the valleys. Air heats above the mountains and rises. Cooler air from the valleys flows in to replace it. Mountain breezes occur at nights because mountains cool faster than the valleys and this cool air nights because mountains cool faster than the valleys and this cool air along the mountains drops and flows along the valleys. Valleys give off heat more slowly and air in them rises, slowly replaced by cooler mountain air.

> If the sun sets clear as a bell,
> Easterly winds you may foretell.
> If the sun behind a bank does set,
> Westerly winds you're sure to get.
> When the rain's before the wind
> Topsail halyards you must mind.
> If the wind's before the rain
> Soon you'll make plain sail again.
> If the wind shifts against the sun
> Trust it not, for back 'twill run.

Fog. Morning fog is simply moisture condensed during a cold night, and it will burn off in the heat of the morning. Night fog or fog late in the day is more the result of cold rain falling through warm air upon which it condenses. This can indicate a future spell of stormy weather.

Precipitation. Rain or snow results from a build up of water vapour or ice crystals within a cloud.

Drizzle is much more dense than rain; it comes out of low layers of cloud and one can expect poor visibility, and relatively warm air to accompany it. Rain may start off as snow, so rain clouds have to be deep and high enough to be really cold. So most of our continuous rain comes from deep cloud layers or fronts.

Clouds are classified into two major categories according to how they are formed:

Cumulus cloud, 'puffy', fair-weather clouds, formed as small areas of rising air.

Stratus cloud, formed in layers when a large area of air is cooled to saturation point.

At the beginning of the nineteenth century clouds were categorized by an English scientist called Luke Howard. In 1803 he presented his cloud classification to his local scientific society. He based his classification on common cloud shapes.

Clouds are also classified by their altitude:

> Cirro or High
> Alto or Middle
> Stratus or Low

High Clouds (above 20,000 ft)
> Cirrus - mares' tails, (above 6 km)
> Cirro-cumulus - sheets or layers
> Cirro-stratus - fine veils, giving halos around sun and moon

Middle Clouds (above 10,000 ft)
> Alto-stratus - sheets of grey dense cloud (2-6 km)
> Alto-cumulus - layers of puffy grey or whitish clouds

Low Clouds (up to 6,500 ft and below 2 km)
> Stratus - low uniform sheet
> Nimbo-stratus - grey, dark, rain-bearing cloud
> Strato-cumulus - irregular mass of clouds

Towering Clouds (up to 75,000 ft)
> Cumulus - puffy, changing shapes
> Cumulo-nimbus - thunder heads

The amateur weather-watcher can get a good idea of what weather to expect by wind-watching. **Wind is defined in two ways, by speed and by direction**
Standing back to the wind, if high clouds come in from the left, weather will usually deteriorate
Standing back to the wind, if high clouds come in from the right, weather should improve.
This rule of thumb applies to people weather-watching in the northern hemisphere. Should you wish to apply this basic observation when in the southern hemisphere merely face the sun and make similar observation of the way high clouds are travelling.

Veering winds indicate that good weather is on its way because when the wind direction changes to the path of the sun or turns clockwise, clearing weather is approaching and winds usually drop.

Backing winds show that a low-pressure system is approaching as the wind direction changes against the path of the sun or turns anticlockwise, usually bringing stronger winds.

Colours in the sky can indicate future trends. Sky colours are the result of interaction between dust particles and water vapour in the atmosphere, and of refraction and diffraction of sunlight through the earth's atmosphere. Shorter violet and blue wavelengths are scattered more effectively than the longer red and orange ones. The combination of all these colours makes blue, but the exact depth of blue depends on the amount of dust and water vapour in the atmosphere. Water droplets and particles of dust encourage the scattering, which has the result of turning the blue a paler shade. Red sunsets are result of the scattering of the yellow, red and orange colours when the sun is lower in the sky and its path is therefore longer.

SUNRISE	
Sky condition	**Weather to be expected**
Grey	Fine
Red	Rain and wind
Light blue	Fine
Dark Blue	Wind
Hard clouds	Wind
Soft clouds	Fine
Clear sky	Maybe rain and wind
High dawn with sun coming over cloud bank	Wind
SUNSET	
Sky condition	**Weather to be expected**
Grey	Rain
Red	Fine
Light blue	Fine
Dark blue	Wind
Hard clouds	Wind
Soft clouds	Fine
Bright yellow	Wind
Pale yellow or green	Rain

Rainbows are produced when sunlight is refracted through spherical raindrops resulting in a distinct band of colour. These usually occur during showery weather when the sun is close to the horizon. The brightest rainbows will be enjoyed when the raindrops are large. Rainbows do not have any great forecasting value, except to warn of a passing shower.

Moonbows are always faint in their colour range, and are caused when light reflected by the moon refracts into visible colours on contact with rain droplets.

Fogbows are almost colourless and occur when sunlight passes through water droplets in fog. Their effect is eerie, like seeing the ghost of a rainbow.

Sun dogs, often known as 'mock suns', are associated with an approaching front and deteriorating weather. They are the result of sunlight passing through layers of ice crystals, and are usually seen as two bright spots on either side of the sun.

Moon dogs, although very rare, are occasionally seen. The best time to see them is just before dawn when the setting moon is low in the western sky and it can shine on the back of a receding rain-cloud. They occur on the night of the full moon.

Haloes, caused by reflection and refraction of light by crystals of ice, often warn of deteriorating weather, and often they appear in association with cirrus clouds.

Weather Lore

Simple observation by country people, turned into rhymes so that they may be more easily remembered, have been collected, as long as men have sailed the oceans, or fished or farmed to make a living. Possibly the most quoted one 'Red sky at night, shepherd's delight' is also on record in the New Testament' Gospel according to St Matthew: **'When it is evening ye say, it will be fair weather, for the sky is red.'** (St Matthew Chap. 16 v.2)

Meteorologists, with instrument readings and satellite information to draw on, may build up a weather picture for a wide area, but the wise countryman, taking his observations from nature, may build up a fairly accurate picture of the weather at the place where it affects him at that point in time. He may notice that **ants**, seemingly aware of changing humidity and barometric pressure, build their nests in circular moulds, high and closed up if rain is approaching, but flattened with holes left open to facilitate ventilation and ant traffic in good weather; he will notice that birds like **swallows and swifts**, flying high and feeding on insects, indicate good weather to come. **Rooks** are seen to fly straight from their nests in good settled weather, but if they turn and twist in the air, rain may be shortly expected. **Fish** feeding close to the surface of the water are a sign of impending rain; **trout** will leap up and feed near the surface water and this is also an indicator of rain because their food, flying insects, will hover just above streams and rivers as the air becomes heavier with increased humidity. Aerobatics and frenzied feeding of all flying creatures is also a sign of approaching rain.

The saying **'calm before the storm'** may relate to the fact that birds, squirrels, crickets and other creatures go quiet, stop mating, fighting or feeding to seek cover before an approaching storm.

If the autumn migration of **swallows and swifts** from U.K. southward takes place earlier than usual, one expects the birds have been made aware of approaching bad weather. The **mistle thrush** is also known as the 'storm cock' because before a storm approaches, it is often heard to sing. In Scotland, the **red-throated diver** has the nickname of 'rain goose' because it is often heard to call ahead of rain. The **stormy petrel** was nicknamed by sailors who associated the appearance of this ocean wanderer with approaching bad weather, and the **snow bunting** has the nickname of 'snow flake' as its appearance often heralds stormy weather. Some birds become noisy and restless before approaching bad weather, especially **crows, woodpeckers and jays**. Birds flying higher is an indication of high pressure. They fly lower when pressure is falling as the air becomes more dense, making it harder to fly. When **sheep** go to the hills and scatter, good weather may be expected, but before a storm they frisk, leap and butt one another. **Crickets** chirp more in high temperatures, but are quieter when the weather cools or a storm is approaching.

Hanging a clump of seaweed outside the back door is one of my childhood memories, and my father always used to check and feel it before starting his gardening activities. Damp seaweed invariably meant moist weather was to be expected.

When leaves show their undersides, rain is on the way. This is because the damp air softens some leaf petioles so that they twist more easily. Many **flowers**, sensitive to humidity, close their petals before the onset of wet weather possibly to protect the pollen in the stamens; the **scarlet pimpernel**, known as the 'poor man's weatherglass', **convolvulus, African marigold, dandelion** and the **ox-eye daisy** all respond ahead of rain by closing their flower heads. The fact that human hay fever sufferers are most uncomfortable during dry fine days is because these are the conditions that encourage grasses and other flowers to release their pollen. Plants are very responsive to a spell of drought. Leaf stoma close to prevent excessive transpiration and wilting, and leaf movements of plants like **marram grasses** curl their laminæ into tubes or other shapes to prevent water loss through the stoma.

In the longer term, plants can adapt to periods of freezing weather and prevent ice crystallising in their tissues by forming insulating layers, such as hairy surfaces, spines or bark. Some plants may dehydrate their tissues to prevent the sap freezing. Some plants develop mechanisms for moving their leaves, so that the petioles can twist or curl to remove the leaves from damaging sun's rays or constant wind tunnels.

Country smells, especially bad ones, become more distinct when pressure is falling. Low barometric pressure allows odours from plants or rotting vegetation to be more easily released into the atmosphere, as this old country saying explains:

'When ditch or pond offend the nose
Look for rain or stormy blows.'

Weather sayings relating to Agriculture

He who sows oats in May gets little that way.
He who mows in May will have neither fruit nor hay.

Calm weather in June sets corn in tune
Midsummer rain spoils hay and grain.

Wet January no wine you'll get.

Cut your thistles before St John and you'll have two instead of one.

Year of snow, crops will grow.

A leafy May and a warm June bring on crops real soon.

No tempest, good July, lest the corn look surly.(Sometimes 'come off bluely'.

Sow beans in the mud and they'll grow like wood.
Sow in the slop, heavy at top.
Sow wheat in dirt and rye in dust.

When the sloe tree is as white as a sheet,
Sow your barley whether it be wet or dry
When the oak puts on its gosling grey,
'Tis time to sow barley night and day.

On Candlemas Day, if the thorn hang a drop,
You're sure of a good crop.

When the elder is white, brew and bake a peck;
When the elder is black, brew and bake a sack.
If leaves hang long on trees expect much frost and snow.

If good apples you would have, the leaves must go into the grave.

When the hawthorn bloom too early show,
We shall have still many snows.

Many haws, many shaws (i.e. hard winter).

Many nuts, many pits (i.e. graves).

Many rains many rowans;
Many rowans many yawns.

Onion skin very thin, mild winter's coming in
Onion skin thick and tough, coming winter cold and rough.

Sow peas and beans in the wane of the moon;
Who soweth them sooner, he soweth too soon.

They that with the planet may rest and rise,
Flourish with bearing most plentifulwise.

A green Christmas brings a heavy harvest.

Light Christmas, light wheatsheaf;
Dark Christmas heavy wheatsheaf.

When bramble bloom in early June
Make early harvest real soon.

Heavy hawthorn blossom, heavy snows to follow.
Many broom blossoms, a fruitful year of corn.

A peck of March dust and a shower in May
Makes the corn green and the fields gay.
A swarm of bees in May
Is worth a load of hay
A swarm of bees in June
Is worth a silver spoon
A swarm of bees in July
Is not worth a fly.

A cherry year, a merry year
A pear year, a dear year
A plum year, a dumb year.

Sea weed dry, sunny sky;
Sea weed wet, rain you'll get.

If we get three frosts before November 11th (All Hallows Eve under the old Gregorian calendar), we'll be sure to have a mild winter.

If after an indifferent new moon the third day is fine, the weather will change for the better in the moon's second quarter.

Never harrow wheat or bean in an East wind.

Fishing is least when wind's in the East.

Ice in November to bear a duck, rest of the winter - slush and muck.

Norwegian Weather Lore Compared

A great Danish friend Ken Jensen, by profession a pilot with Scandinavian Airlines, and a very experienced Wayfarer sailor, told me of a book written by a Norwegian meteorologist, Toril Torki, called:

Old Weather Signs for New Weather Projects.

Ken translated some of the weather signs into English. They show a remarkable similarity to our own weather lore.

1. When the sheep go out to the hills, the weather will be nice. When the sheep go home, the weather will soon rain. (Explanation - the sheep feel the humidity in their wool.)
2. When the fields clear of snow before the road, it will be an early spring. (This is because the frost in the soil has already left and new precipitation will therefore drain down.)
3. When the magpie builds her nest low it will be a rainy summer; if the bird builds high, it will be a fine summer.

4. When the swallows come early the spring is imminent.
5. When the wild geese are going south, the prevailing north winds are just around the corner.
6. When the swallows fly low, a low pressure front is coming in.
7. When the seabirds fly in from the sea, bad weather will follow.
8. When the raven flies screaming in from the sea, death is out there.
9. When it is showery, the cattle and horses will turn their backs towards wind and rain, and may even stop feeding.
10. Wind direction is indicated from the way the noses of the wild animals are pointing.
11. When the chimney smoke goes straight up, the weather is stable, but when it starts to bend, a change is approaching.
12. When the ground fog stays low, the weather is stable, but when it starts to climb up the hill rain may be expected.
13. A ring (halo) around the sun means rain will come.
14. Morning red gives evening wet.
    Evening red gives morning sweet.
15. White moon full gives nice weather, yellow moon full gives foul.
16. Polar light visible gives clear, cool weather - and wind before rain shows good weather is on its way.
17. Rain before wind indicates bad weather - and wind before rain shows good weather is on its way.
18. When sun sets into a sack (*saek*) it comes up in a brook (*baek*) i.e. weather coming in from the West.
19. Early morning fog will give a fine day.
20. With the wind from behind you and the high clouds moving across from the left, weather will be bad (i.e. low pressure warning), with the wind behind you and high clouds moving across from the right - weather will be good.
21. Thunder from the sea is bad, but thunder from over the valley or land is reasonable.

Weather Sayings Relating to Poor Weather

When birds and badgers are fat in October, expect a cold winter.

Clear moon, frost soon.

January wet, no wine you'll get.

When March has April weather, April will have March weather.

St Swithin's day (July 15th) if ye do rain, for forty days it will remain.

Frost on the shortest day indicates a severe winter.

Red sky in the morning is a warning.

If the sky goes pale to bed 'twill rain tomorrow it is said.

Rainbow to leeward, foul fares the day.

When leaves show their underside, be very sure that rain betides.

Rope is more difficult to untwist before a storm.

When black snails on the road you see, then on the morrow rain will be.

When trout refuse to bait or fly, there ever is a storm a-nigh.

When pigs carry sticks, the clouds will play tricks,
When they lie in the mud, no fears of a flood.

Rainbows in the eastern sky, the morrow will be dry
Rainbows in the west that gleams - rain falls in the streams.

If the cock crows going to bed, he will certainly rise with watery head.

Seagull, seagull, sit on the sand;
It's never good weather if you're on the sand.

When sheep do huddle by tree and bush,
Bad weather's coming with wind and slush.

When fleas do very many grow, then 'twill surely rain and snow.

A fly on your nose, you'll slap and it goes;
If it comes again it will bring good rain.

Gnats bite and I scratch in vain, because they know it's going to rain.

The goose and the gander begin to meander,
The matter is plain – they're dancing for rain.

When grass is dry at morning light - look for rain before the night.

The circle of the sun wets the shepherd.

The moon with a circle brings water in her beak;
The bigger the ring the nearer the wet.

Rainbows to windward foul fares the day.
Rainbows to leeward damp runs away.

Rain long foretold long past. Short notice soon will pass.

Mare's tails and mackerel scales make lofty ships carry low sails.

Curls that kink and cords that bind - signs of rain and wind.

The farther the sight the nearer the rain.

Mackerel clouds in the sky,
Expect more wet than dry.

Mackerel scales - Furl your sails.

Ants that move their eggs and climb,
Rain coming any time.

A bad winter is betide if hair grows thick as a bear's hide.

If bees stay at home, rain will come soon.
If they fly away fine will be the day.

Trace the sky the painter's brush
The winds around you soon will rush.

When the donkey blows his horn,
'Tis time to house your hay and corn.

Fireflies fly low before a rain.

Earthworms appear, rain will follow.

Martins fly low before rain.

When swans fly against the wind, rain is coming.

When cocks crow and then drink,
Rain and thunder is on the brink.

A winter's fog will freeze a hog.

An old cat frisking like a kitten foretells a storm.

Evening grey, morning red, brings rain down upon your head.

When the wind veers towards the sun,
Trust it not for back 'twill run.

When the glass falls low, prepare for a blow.

When cattle stand with backs to wind, rain is coming.

Rainbow in morn, bad weather in store.
Sun goes down clear as a bell, bad weather sure as hell.

If squirrel early starts to hoard,
Winter will pierce us like a sword.

If cows lie down early in the morning, it will rain by night.

When grass is dry at morning light, look for rain before the night.

When the days begin to lengthen, the cold begins to strengthen.

Cold is the night when stars shine bright.

When snow falls dry, it means to lie,
But flakes light and soft, bring rain oft.

Sounds travelling far and wide, a stormy day will betide.

I know ladies by the score whose hair like seaweed scents the storm.

A coming storm your shooting corns presage,
And aches will throb, your hollow teeth rage.

If the oak is out before the ash, 'twill be a winter of wet and splash.
If the ash precede the oak, then you may expect a soak.

A wet Good Friday - very little hay.

If St Vitus day (June 15th) be rainy, it will rain for 30 days together.

When the clouds are upon the hills, they'll come down by the mills.

When the wind is in the east, 'tis good for neither man nor beast.
When the wind is in the north, the skilful fisher goes not forth.
When the wind's in the south, the rain's in its mouth.

When clouds appear like rocks and towers,
The earth's refreshed by frequent showers.

When the ass begins to bray, be sure we shall have rain that day.

When frogs moan, it will rain soon.

Fish bite least when wind is in the east.

Gnats bite and I scratch in vain because they know 'tis going to rain.

Seaweed wet, rain you'll get.

If ants their walls do frequent build,
Rain from clouds will soon be spilled.

If cold on St Peter's day (February 22nd) it will last longer than normal.

If it freezes on St Matthias' day (February 24th) it will freeze for a month.

Fields full of birds, bad weather on way.

Red sky at morning, shepherd's warning.

Long foretold long passed,
Short notice, soon past.

When down of dandelion close up it's a sign of rain.
Evening grey and morning red will bring down rain upon your head.

When the wind shifts against the sun
Trust it not for it will rain.

At sea with a low and falling glass
Soundly sleeps a careless ass.

February fill dyke, be it black or white.
If Candlemas be fair and clear
There'll be two winters in the year.

A February spring isn't worth a pin.

When the wind shifts to the west early in June, expect wet weather until the end of August.

A green Christmas makes a fat churchyard.

On Saturday new, on Sunday full (the moon)
Has never brought good, nor never will.

Twinkling stars, a sign of wind.

When the stars begin to huddle, the earth will soon be a puddle.

Rainbow at morn, fair weather all gorn.

If Candlemas be fair and bright, winter will have another flight.

Mackerel sky, not long dry.

A red moon will blow; a pale moon will rain, a white moon - no rain or snow.

Two moons in May – 'twill rain for a year and a day.

Sayings Related to Fine Weather

St Swithin's day if ye be fair for 40 days 'twill rain nae mair
St Swithin's day if ye do rain, for 40 days it will remain.

A leaking May and warm June bring in a harvest very soon.

Red sky at night, shepherd's delight.

Calm weather in June sets corn in tune.

Rainbow to leeward damp runs away.

When spiders weave their webs by noon, fine weather is coming soon.

If the sky beyond the cloud is blue,
Be glad, there's a picnic for you.

When the dew is on the grass, rain will never come to pass.

Expect fine weather if larks fly high and sing long.

When a cock crows after a shower, clear weather is coming.

Swallows fly high - clear blue sky
Swallows fly low - rain we shall know

When starlings and crows group together, expect rain.

A summer fog will roast a dog.

If a cat washes its face behind the ear,
'Tis a sign that weather will be fine and clear.

No weather or ill when winds are still.

If bees fly away, fine will be the day.

Evening red morning grey sets the traveller on his way.

When the glass rises high, let your kite fly.

When a squirrel eats nuts in a tree, weather is warm as warm can be.

If the ash is out before the oak then we'll scarcely have a soak – 'twill
be a summer of fire and smoke.
If the oak's before the ash then you'll only get a splash.

Plenty of ladybirds, plenty of hope.

St Matthew's day (September 21st) bright and clear, bring good wine
in next year.

Dry Lent - fertile year.

If St Romanus' day (February 28th) be bright and clear, August will
be a goodly year.

Rain before seven - fine before eleven.

A sunny shower won't last half an hour.

When the wind is in the south it blows the bait into fish's mouth,
When the wind is in the west, then 'tis at its very best.

When ground lark soar high on a cloudy day, clearing skies will follow.

When swallows' fleets soar high and sport the air –
He told us that the wet would soon be clear.
When spiders weave their webs by noon, fine weather is coming soon.

Seaweed dry - sunny sky.

Hoar frost and gypsies never stay nine days in a place.

If there be a profuse dew in summer, that day will be fine.
A white frost never lasts more than three days.

If rain begins at early morning light,
'Twill end ere day at noon is bright.

March buys winter's coat and sells it three days afterward.

The greater the haze the more settled the weather.

Expect fine weather if larks fly high and sing long.

When a cock crows after a shower, clear weather is coming.

If westerly winds are strong and Candlemas Day (February 2nd)
brings cloud and rain, then winter is gone and won't come again.

At sea with a low and rising glass
Sleeps soundly a careful wise one.

The nearer the burr the farther the storm.

August thunder promises fat grapes and fine vintages.

If October bring much frost and wind
Then January and February will be fair and kind.

If November ice will bear a duck
There'll be nothing after but sludge and muck.

Near burr far rain
Far burr near rain (Burr is a ring around the moon).

Bright stars indicate good weather.

A rainbow at night - fair weather in sight.

Glass high. Fine weather.

***Wanderer* in 'loomy' weather (see page 44)**

Men who watch the Weather at Sea

Barry Coe
Cockle Fisherman, Bait Digger, Caravan Site Employee.

Barry is a Norfolk man who has spent a lifetime on the shore. Bait-digging and cockle-raking are his specialities. 'It was a good life,' commented Barry, 'but my father used to say, "Boy, you want to get into the leisure trade if you want a job for keeps, because that is where the growth is going to be."' Nowadays, Barry works on the Wells holiday caravan park, owned by Tom Coke.

'Bait-digging was good thirty years ago,' said Barry. 'There was enough work for many diggers. We sent worms all over the country, but that time has long gone. In the 1950s the fishing port of Wells also was famous for its fleet of sprat boats and several whelk boats, but nowadays, there are more crabs than whelks to be harvested off Wells.' Asking the reason, I was told that whelks used to breed well locally, living on plankton, but the mud they thrived on has been churned up and sand has replaced it.

Barry's father kept a daily record of the weather for many years, and he passed on his observations to his son. 'It's going to be a miserable day, not worth going out to sea,' he would say to his son, as they watched a yellow sky dawning.

'Sure enough, there'd be wind and rain by midday,' said his son. A mackerel sky, or a green tinge in the sky, were also pointers to wind and rain approaching. Barry also told me about 'wind dogs', little black lumps of clouds in a darkening sky. He also endorsed what other fishermen had said about sighting 'sun dogs' and expecting stormy weather to follow.

'It's getting harder to predict the weather,' said Barry. 'Things don't work out like they used to. We also get our own peculiar weather on this part of the coast, because we stick our snouts out into the North Sea. The only time we get really bad weather is when it comes in from Russia, but now we don't get nearly so many easterly winds as we used to. There's no guarantee now; climate is changing. Some call it global warming, others say it's due to cycles of change, but it's not going to be all that much fun, a lot more wind and rain than we used to get and unpredicted stormy episodes in future years.'

27

'My dad used to be brilliant. I don't know how he did it, but sometimes he'd be pretty accurate two or three months in advance. When we used to go out worm-digging, we'd go all over the place into the Wash, and we'd often be up at dawn. If it were raining at 06.00 hours I might say, "It's no good going today, look at the weather," but he would reply, "It'll be fine by the time we get there," and invariably if we went thirty miles off, it would be fine with the sun shining as we drove by Lynn. Then another time we'd return and father would say, "We won't be here tomorrow. Look at all those lights in the sky. Visibility is too good, you can see all the lights as far away as Skegness. It'll be blowing hard from the north-west tomorrow." He was rarely wrong.'

'Working at sea you have to watch the weather all the time; you have to rely on all the signs around you, and make up your mind yourself. Weather forecasts often do not take into account our local conditions,' said Barry, and he told me that if the sun rises really yellow, 'yary' they call it, it would be a pretty miserable day, blowing and raining by midday onwards.

Barry's father used to tell his son, during spring and summer, if the sun came up pink with red streaks right across the sky it would be fine all day. 'How far has the red gone over?' he would ask, then would predict 'Old red's gone halfway over the sky, it'll be fine till lunch time.'

One of his favourite sayings was, 'Easterly wind, fishing's least, westerly wind, fishing's best.'

He also maintained that on the 21st of 'the October month', if the wind was a light north or north-west, it would continue that direction broadly, until the spring equinox.

Barry said his father watched the behaviour of birds a lot. In wintertime if the whooper swans came inland, it was a sign of an approaching depression, and he was invariably correct; rain or snow or wind would sweep in from the north-east within a day or two of the arrival of the swans. A 'cock's eye' always told him that wind and rain could be expected within twenty-four hours. He called a little rainbow in the sky a 'cock's eye'. 'Wind dogs' he described as little black bits of clouds all broken up; that too indicated wind and rain on its way. A 'mackerel-backed' sky, little scales piling up in the sky, meant the same thing, an approaching depression.

Barry Coe at work digging for bait

'We used to go out at midnight, going along the shore for trout or salmon,' recalled his son, 'lovely nights. Then Dad would say, "Look at all those lights. You can see right out in the Wash. We'll have tomorrow night in our beds.'

David Cox
Lifeboat Coxswain, Whelk Fisherman

David was born in Wells-next-the-Sea and is now in his mid-seventies. The family were Sheringham fishermen, very well known for their success in crabbing, cockling, long-lining, and herring fishing in the autumn.

'My grandfather came to Wells because there were too many fishermen in Sheringham,' said David. 'Part of the family emigrated to Grimsby, but my grandfather decided on Wells. One day, he and a fisherman from Sheringham, Harry Wilson, were walking around the whelk sheds at East Quay, when they were challenged by a man who wanted to know what they were doing there. They got into conversation, and the man turned out to be Lord Leicester who owned the land as part of the Holkham estate; there were brickworks along the East Quay then. As a result of that chance meeting the Cox family rented some land, which included the old brickworks drying sheds, which they wanted to use for fishing gear, also to boil the shellfish. The Bayfield family and the Grimes family rented the old brick-house. The Cox family eventually took over all three brick-houses and began a family fishing business. In the winter months, several fishermen had mussel lays in Wells harbour where they cultivated mussels, laid in the springtime as seed mussels which they gathered from Heacham and Hunstanton.'

David worked at the Globe Hotel when he left the local school at fourteen. His job was bottling beer, but he was mad to go to sea. 'I was fourteen when the war broke out, and I got on a merchant ship as deck boy. I went across the Atlantic, New York and back. It took us twenty-three days from Belfast to New York travelling in a six-knot convoy. An interesting experience, but I got homesick and returned home.' A year later David, with all the local boys, had a medical.

'You've passed A1,' reported a board official, 'a place for you will be found in the Army.'

'Oh no, I'm going to sea,' retorted the young man. Eventually he got an official document telling him he should continue fishing as his part in the war effort until a vacancy came up in the Royal Navy. David automatically joined the Wells lifeboat crew and continued fishing with the older men in his family. 'I was keen to learn and used to watch and listen to my grandfather and uncle. The sea was in my blood.'

David recalled one trip when he was at sea with 'Loady'. He always put his faith in the 'glass' (barometer), and it had been falling. 'We were out at dawn,' said David, 'when I asked my uncle, "What's that bright light?"' 'That's Cromer Light, and we're going home,' replied his uncle. 'The visibility was very good, some twenty-two miles from Wells to Cromer. Sure enough, within the hour a gale sprang up,' said David. 'From then on, I always put my faith in the barometer.'

'All last week (mid-February 2001) the glass was high, 1046 millibars. If you have a high glass and it falls rapidly, you know there's funny weather coming in. If you have a low glass, and the reading rises rapidly, then you'll look for a gale of wind in an hour or two.'

'We had no up-to-date radio weather forecasts, so the best guide was the barometer. There used to be one on Wells Quay; it was placed there by the Royal Lifeboat Institution because so many fishermen's lives were being lost at sea. My grandfather used to come down to West Quay, consult the barometer there and say, 'My boys, you're not going to sea today, there's some bad weather coming in.'

David described one time when they got the weather wrong and were caught out. 'We went out one morning and there was a kind of drizzly rain, more like a mist. As we went down the slip one fisherman remarked, "There's talk of bad weather coming in, but I guess we have time to get out, get our pots and be in before it arrives. The sea was like a millpond as we went off, but there was a vicious black cloud to the north. Everywhere turned black before we got to our pots, then the wind came up; you could see it starting to blow, little dabs on the water. We hauled in two shanks, about 72 pots, with the wind increasing all the time, then the sea got up. Suddenly a big sea came over our stern and knocked me off my feet. My crew were knocked over too, so we left the rest of the pots, pulled up sail, a heavy canvas lug sail, to steady the boat and made for home. We were about sixteen miles off, and a north-west gale came through that quick.'

David told me that the swell always came in before the wind, and that was what the fisherman always looked out for. 'You can always tell,' he said. 'If it's been a fine day and we've hauled in our pots, with six to seven miles to the harbour, with the tide on the make, you can always tell what it's going to be like the next day, because if the swell is there, there'll be no sea trip the next day.'

David told me about a time when the lifeboat was called out in extraordinarily bad conditions. 'It was a Thursday, February 15th 1979; it had been snowing that night in a breeze of wind, but nothing too bad. The maroons went off and we got to the lifeboat house at 10.30 a.m. The Sheringham and Cromer boats couldn't be launched, but the Humber lifeboat was launched. A Romanian vessel was in danger of breaking her back on the Race Bank, and the tide was ebbing. She had lost two anchors and also her engine power.'

As Wells coxswain, David had eight crew (there should have been seven). He said to his crew 'This is no job for us.' However, they all wanted to have a go, so the Oakley lifeboat was launched and they went down the harbour to see what conditions were like. 'It was two hours after high water with an easterly blowing hard,' recalled David.

David Cox (left) and Anthony Jordan (right) first and second cox of the Wells Lifeboat

He then described, in a most matter-of-fact manner, how they were going full throttle at eight knots. 'We were without radio or radio position as a heavy sea took away our aerial. I took a compass course and the time as we left the harbour, and we steamed on for two hours.' It started to snow heavily, making the radar useless. Heavy seas swept over the lifeboat; they were pitching heavily - they had head winds north-east. Finding the stricken vessel, just a shadow in 30 yards visibility, Wells lifeboat stood by until fifteen hundred hours. They got the drogue ready, wrestling with frozen ropes. Finally an Aran 54ft, a much bigger lifeboat, arrived on the scene from the Humber, and the much smaller Wells boat was relieved. 'Too bloody late - it was just after fifteen hundred hours,' said David. 'That was our worst time, because we had to run. Twenty-five fathom of rope was let out on the drogue, and we came across the Race Bank in breaking seas. I've never seen the sea so violent as that day.'

Unlike entering the Humber or making for Yarmouth, to enter the drying harbour of Wells a seaman needed daylight. 'Steaming at half speed, trailing a drogue with a huge sea running, the boat felt comfortable,' recalled David. On shore they thought the boat had foundered, because there was no radar or radio contact for three hours with the lifeboat. At nineteen hundred hours one of the crew thought he saw a light. By then the blizzard-like conditions were down and the snow had stopped. Coming home on a south-west course with no idea where they were, the chances of finding an unlit harbour were slim, but at 19.30 hours, a flare was put up. A message came through loud and clear, 'Wells lifeboat, this is Scolt One, Brancaster Coastguard. You are laying about a mile north of Brancaster. We have seen your flare...' 'That gave me a bearing straight away, so I put the helm hard over, and taking the beam seas it took us two hours to reach Wells Harbour,' said David - even thirty years on he lived the drama of that day deeply.

'There was a heavy sea running,' continued David. 'A fishing boat came down the harbour and laid there with all her lights on, to guide us to the lifeboat house. We were running three-quarter speed with thirty foot of drogue out. The men had no food that day - nobody wanted anything. I was on the wheel all day, too busy watching the seas to want food. I was all of a tremble for two days after we returned. You never really relax 'til about four days after the trip.'

David took over the lifeboat as cox from his uncle. 'I went to sea fishing with him, and he put me through it, and told me all I know about the sea and the weather. The sea has been my life, and I've enjoyed it.'

David never goes to sea now. He retired from the lifeboat after

33

forty years service. He went to London in the May of the year of the dramatic lifeboat launch, to receive the Silver award; after that he was awarded the Bronze Medal. Forty-three years service in the lifeboat.'

'Fishing has gone from Wells as a livelihood. You have to go so far out. We used only to have to go out for two hours, at the back of the Race. Now they have to go off for three and a half hours – that's seven hours there and back. There were five whelk boats here when I first started; we'd have our winter and summer grounds, so the fish were being conserved. Nowadays, the grounds are damaged by the trawlers. Trawling's done a lot of damage, pulling all the spawn about and ruining the grounds.'

Asked about the changing weather patterns, David pointed out that a backing wind was no good on this coast. If the weather was fine, with the morning wind westerly, then it went round to north-west, then came off south-east at nights, but if the wind backed, went south-east, then east, it would never be fine the following day. I was also told that many years ago the easterly winds lasted in the spring for many weeks, but in more recent times, the winds have been south-west for much of the time, and the winters and springs much less intensely cold latterly.

Other signs I was told about related to gulls. Gulls sitting about in the fields meant bad weather was coming in, and the same thing applied to the behaviour of Brent geese.

The making tides usually brought in bad weather - it rarely came in on the ebb. A gale never coincided with a nine-metre tide, but bad weather often came in on seven to eight-metre tides. Wind will always come through on the making tides, and that was when flooding could be expected.

'Local conditions often make a mockery of the radio forecasts,' said David. 'You simply need to be on the spot to see what's happening.' He described being at sea in summer time with a fresh easterly wind, hauling pots some fifteen miles out. 'That would be bad winds for hauling pots, especially with the tide going westerly.' However, once inside Blakeney Overfalls the easterly wind would often die, with the wind going southerly. 'Local winds are all to do with the land and sea breezes and the heat of the land,' said David.

I was told that if the tides were running hard, a difference in the catch was noticeable, and that the best tides for good whelking were about six-metre tides. 'If the tides are running hard and the current running on the bottom, the pots will tremble and whelks won't go in

34

the pots for the bait.' He also said that fishing was better on slack tides and early morning tides, and the same rule applied to line fishing. Easterly winds in summertime meant that the swell took a long time getting out of the sea. One hundred bushels of whelks, a normal day's catch, could be reduced to half that if the easterly winds were prolonged.

'Modern fishermen don't go out in bad weather these days. They also have the comfort of a wheel-house and modern boats are faster. In our old heavy boats, which were slower, we only had a dodger for protection from the weather. So these days, the weather is not the all-important issue.'

David said that, in the old times when they set out in the early morning, if they could see *Dudgeon* light vessel, which was fifteen miles away, it always meant they could expect bad weather coming in. The same could be expected if the fishermen saw 'sun dawgs' or 'pheasants' eyes' - a light halo either side of the sun. Within twenty-four hours you'd get wind or rain.

Fishermen were also superstitious about the weather and would never talk about pigs when getting ready to go to sea. It always talked up bad weather!

Several of David's fishing partners and past lifeboat crew have similar things to say about David: 'He is an incredible fisherman. He's a brilliant seaman.'

Henry Davies - 'Shrimp'

Crab Fisherman, Cromer Lifeboat Coxswain

The R.N.L.I. Henry Blogg museum has been situated in the number two boat house at Cromer since 1967. The lifeboat currently housed in this museum is the Watson Class *H. F. Bailey.* This boat served at Cromer from 1935 to 1945, the World War Two years. Under the command of Henry Blogg, the boat was launched over 120 times saving the lives of some 520 men.

Henry Blogg joined the Cromer Lifeboat crew in January 1894, at the age of eighteen years. When he retired in September 1947 he had served on the boat for 53 years, 37 of them as coxswain. Henry Blogg was born in a cottage at New Street, Cromer. He went to the local Goldsmith's School. At the age of eleven, becoming top boy scholar, he left because his stepfather needed him on the crab boat. At the age of eighteen Henry joined the lifeboat crew, becoming coxswain in 1909. During his service of 53 years he was awarded the Institute's Gold Medal three times and the Silver Medal four times, plus a host of other awards. His record is unequalled in the history of the lifeboat service.

'Shrimp' Davies, also christened Henry after his uncle, no doubt grew up very aware of the tenacity of purpose that his uncle exhibited. I met Shrimp on a sparkling sunny day on Cromer beach. He was sitting beside his shed, hiring beach chairs to the holiday-makers looking out on a calm blue sea. The local man who directed me to Shrimp's site said, 'He's a legend here. He was coxswain of the Cromer Lifeboat for close on thirty years.' Very quickly I became charmed by his incredible memory, ready wit, and wholesome laughter. His natural modesty gave little indication that I was listening to a legend.

'How did you get your nickname?' I asked of this well-built eighty-seven-year-old, jovial gentleman of the sea. Shrimp roared with laughter. 'When I was born, I only weighed about four pounds; my uncle Henry came to see my mother and told her I looked like a little shrimp. The nickname has stuck ever since.' Their close-knit family was much in evidence, both in Shrimp's conversation and in the interruptions of our talk on the sea front by his oldest great-granddaughter who, on her way to work at a nearby café, stopped to give her great-grandfather a hearty kiss. 'Don't be late for work,' he told her. Later Shrimp's nephew, Richard, called by to chat to his uncle, before going on to launch Cromer's longshore lifeboat at the start of Cromer RNLI's Open and Fund Raising Day. Richard, the present coxswain of the lifeboat, took over from his uncle in 1976, just as Shrimp had taken over the post from his uncle Henry Blogg in 1947.

'If you come from a fishing family, you don't volunteer for the lifeboats,' said Shrimp dryly. 'You are expected to join. In 1931 I was just two days off being seventeen. The Sheringham lifeboat got into trouble; uncle and father went to the Cromer lifeboat launch, and I followed and picked up a crew lifebelt. Uncle Harry told me to give up the lifebelt as I wasn't seventeen. I was quite angry.'

Shrimp left school at fourteen and went straight to sea, working with his uncle Henry Blogg, hauling pots with cast-iron bottoms; twenty-five in a shank, with fifteen fathoms (95 ft) of wet rope between each pot, soon gave the young boy blisters. A week after leaving school Shrimp chanced to meet his old school teacher. 'How's the job?' he was asked, and for reply Shrimp held out his hands. 'Oh, my God, I didn't do that, did I?' said the school teacher in mock horror. 'I used to get the cane plenty of times,' said Shrimp, chuckling at the memory.

'I was seasick every time I went to sea, then came home and ate like a horse. After four years I took on a young chap of eighteen, then was never sick again. I was also sick every time I went out in the lifeboat, but when I became cox'n in 1947, I was never sick again.' Surprising confessions from a great seaman.

The conversation turned to weather. 'Normal bad weather signs are sundogs and weather headings,' explained Shrimp who described a weather heading as a little square of light that had all the colours of the rainbow in it. 'You can be sure of wind and rain if you see either of these. The bad weather will normally come in from the direction in which you see the weather heading, and it is normally seen just above the horizon. Sundogs, false suns, haloes of light either side of the true sun, always mean wind and rain coming in within twenty-four hours,' said Shrimp. 'Those signs never fail to warn you.'

'The old fishermen hated to see crows,' said Shrimp, 'because they were usually the forerunners of difficult weather, usually onshore winds. I made up a ditty:-

When the crows from Cromer beach you see
The wind will blow in from the sea.
It might be light, it might be strong
But those old crows are never wrong.
If you see then just a few
Then it'll blow force one or two
But if there's ten or more
Then 'twill blow force eight or more
And if over their nests they circle high
Be sure an onshore wind is nigh.'

Seagulls, too, seemed to sense bad weather because they would congregate on the foreshore. Crabs seemed aware of bad weather on the way, because they would hang on the net around the top of the pots. In the old pots, whipping was used to brace the willow uprights together and to fix the 'crinny' to stop the crabs escaping, and the crabs would try to chew a hole to escape back to their holes having eaten the bait in the pots. Should the chewed rope not be spotted and mended before the pot was next baited up, the next trapped crabs would go to the worn spot to try to escape before bad weather blew up.

Shrimp talked about watching the sky for weather indicators. 'You sometimes see the sky a little lighter than you should. Be sure you'll get a gale of wind from that direction shortly,' he said. 'Mare's tails always tell of wind on the way,' he said with complete conviction. 'Sometimes you see clouds bunching up like a shepherd's flock...cirrus clouds bundling up to look like a flock. That's a sure sign of rain within twenty-four hours.' Then he quoted, 'Shepherd's flocks and mare's tails make tall ships carry small sails.'

If the sky turned red in the morning or late in the evening, rain should be expected. 'The old fishermen used to say the sky had a "curious hue",' said Shrimp with a chuckle. A bronze/yellow sky or a

38

green always told of bad weather on its way.

'The old fishermen always consulted the barometer,' said Shrimp. 'The wind never freshens when the glass is going back, but when the glass goes low then suddenly jumps up, then there's going to be a gale of wind.'

'Sharp rise after low foretells a stronger blow - right every time,' said Shrimp with authority. 'There were no forecasts when we started fishing - all we had was the weather glass and our observations. All we wanted to know clearly was, could we get to our gear, get the crabs and get back safely. One day some of the old men didn't want to go to sea, and so took the glass and held it close to the cabin fire, but my uncle wasn't taken in. Sometimes you can see a hard line along the horizon - very clear visibility - then you can be sure of a strong easterly on the way; there's always a bad wind on this coast. A halo round the moon was an indication of rain on the way. 'Near burr far rain, far burr near rain,' quoted Shrimp.

'In years gone by, fishing off the beach was quite dangerous and each man watched to see if the other boats were preparing to go out. One day in 1953, I was with my younger brother Bob in one boat, and my older brother Jim was in another boat. Jim said 'I don't like the look of it.' 'Right,' said Shrimp. 'Then I'm going home.' However, the two brothers went out, because Jim remarked 'I suppose if they are going out we'd better go too.' 'Jim should have trusted his own judgement and listened to his own instincts. He'd have been alive today,' said Shrimp. The wind and sea came up quickly, and he drowned.

'Sometimes you are fishing on a quiet sea then the swell comes in, and surf seems to be breaking on the beach,' said Shrimp, 'then you know you're in for a gale of wind. One day I was out fishing with my uncle Henry and saw the wind coming in from Norway, and I remarked, "Now is the winter of our discontent!" He corrected me, by quoting the whole of that speech from Shakespeare's *Richard III*, but when I interrupted and told him what I'd seen, he said, "Oh my God, we'd better get out of here!"' Shrimp fished with his uncle for twenty years. I asked if he enjoyed it. His immediate response was, 'Of course. It was a good life - out in the fresh air all the time...You must have faith in the Lord, faith in your crew and faith in your boat.' There was not a trace of sentimentality as he went on 'And you grow to love your boat.' His boat was locally built, an open one, named after his wife Kathleen and his two daughters Patricia and Catherine.

39

That boat still works at Blakeney.

I asked Shrimp about the various weather forecasts the modern coxswain and fishermen could utilise today. 'They don't seem able to get it right all the time,' he said impatiently. Then, roaring with laughter at the memory, he recalled when a visitor said to him,

'Good morning. It's going to rain today.'

'No ma'am,' he replied, 'it's not going to rain today.'

'My friend Michael told me it would rain today,' she retorted.

'That man couldn't forecast the result of a one-horse race,' he said, 'and it didn't rain that day, nor did it the next,' he concluded with satisfaction.

Norfolk seems to generate its own weather - and it's very localised. Shrimp quoted:-

'When the wind is in the west - weather at its very best

When the wind is in the eas, 'tis fit for neither man nor beast.'

As we made ready to take our leave of this grand old man of the sea, whose knowledge of this part of the coast must be matchless, I asked him to tell me the worst lifeboat weather he had experienced. With no hesitation he described the rescue of August 6th, 1941.

It was bloody dangerous; six of us were washed into the sea. The wind was force 10. The sea - well, if I described it to you, you'd think I was exaggerating, or telling lies.'

A week after my interview with Shrimp Davies, the following account was published in the *Eastern Daily Press* because it was sixty years ago to the week that this amazing rescue took place.

On the morning of August 6 1941, Shrimp Davies was sitting in his home in Cromer. "I hadn't been to sea crabbing that morning, because the sea was too rough," he remembers.

At 8am, he got the call all lifeboat crewmen expect, and made his way to the Cromer boathouse.

The 27-year-old fisherman had no idea where he was headed, and was given no indication by Cromer's legendary coxswain, Henry Blogg.

"He never told us where we were going until we launched, because of the wartime secrecy."

All he knew was that German E-boats sought any chance they could to target convoys of merchant ships and their vital cargoes, as they were escorted along "safe" corridors by the Royal Navy.

But this time, it was not torpedoes or mines which had ripped into the convoy.

As they powered eastwards along the north Norfolk coast in the HF Bailey, Henry Blogg told his men several ships had run aground on the southern end of the Middle Haisbro.

"We're going to see something today we've never seen before," Shrimp told his father and fellow crewman Billy Davies.

They came across six ships, stricken on the sands, being battered by the stormy sea.

A destroyer and its whaler had started rescue work, but 12 seamen were already dead.

"When they first went on the sandbank it must have been rougher than when we got there, because the steamers nearly all had their backs broken," he said.

Only the funnel and upper deck of the nearest boat, the Oxshott, was above the waves, so the crew decided to head for the nearby Gallois.

"The captain of that one waved us to go back to the Oxshott because they were in a more dangerous position."

Turning back, they realised 16 sailors were hanging on to the funnel of the Oxshott by ropes.

"We couldn't believe there was anyone round the funnel. It's amazing any of them had survived,"

It was at that moment that Henry Blogg decided to use a breathtakingly bold manoeuvre.

"He drove on top of the sinking deck of the Oxshott, and my father got the grapplings to run across the deck."

One by one, all 16 were saved.

Then Blogg skilfully brought the H F Bailey alongside the Gallois, and 31 men slid down ropes or jumped on to the deck.

Forty-seven exhausted but relieved sailors were placed on a destroyer before the H F Bailey turned for a third steamer, the Deerwood.

Once again 19 men jumped aboard after the lifeboat drove on to its submerged deck.

By this time the second Cromer lifeboat, the Harriot Dixon, had reached the scene and Shrimp's uncle Jack Davies transferred to the smaller boat to take over as coxswain.

He maintained a similarly brave position against the bridge of the steamer Taara to rescue the eight remaining men aboard.

The Cromer crews were not alone – the Great Yarmouth and Gorleston lifeboat, the Louise Stephens, arrived at 11.30am and with great difficulty went alongside the steamer's lee side; ropes were thrown and the entire crew of 23 were taken off.

Two other lifeboats, the Foresters Centenary of Sheringham and the Michael Stephens of Lowestoft, later arrived to find the rescue had finished.

But for the crew of the H F Bailey, any thoughts of home had to wait till they had rescued the 22 crewmen of the sixth and final steamer, Paddy Hendly.

With the job almost complete, the worst moment of the rescue arrived.

Heavily-laden with 51 men, the lifeboat twice bumped on the Sands and then ran aground.

"Waves were breaking all the time. Had another one broken on top of us we would probably all have been washed overboard.

"But the next big wave lifted us off the sand."

"Anyone who says they haven't been afraid in a lifeboat is a liar. We were a bit scared at the time."

The relieved crew of the H F Bailey transferred the remaining 41 sailors to a destroyer, and with the Louise Stephens made its way to Yarmouth, while the Harriot Dixon returned to Cromer.

Their actions had saved 119 lives – 88 by Shrimp's crew, one the highest numbers ever by a single lifeboat.

"I got home in the afternoon and first thing I did was kiss my wife Kathleen and the children," said Shrimp, who with the rest of the crew was decorated by the RNLI.

Allen Frary
Wells Lifeboat Coxswain

Allen's father was a lorry driver, but at weekends he took holiday makers to the cockle beds off the harbour. The trip cost them sixpence return, and the ferry was an old ship's lifeboat. Allen's boyhood was by the shore. He went eel-babbing with his father and long-shoring for mullet and trout in Holkham Bay. Sometimes his grandfather took him cockle-raking in West Lake. The young boy raked up the cockles and put them in a sack. In all weathers on a Saturday afternoon, Allen helped and was given 3d pocket money. His grandfather sold the cockles as well as mussels, winkles and samphire to all the villages within a ten-mile radius of Wells.

Leaving school he wanted to see the world and so joined the

Merchant Navy as a trainee cook. To qualify he got work experience in a local bakery. His first ship was out of Felixstowe, exporting Ford cars from Dagenham to Scandinavia. He had taken his father's advice 'If you want to see the world, do it on a full stomach.'

Next, Allen did three six-month trips on a general cargo boat going down to New Zealand, and enjoyed the experience a great deal. The dock strikes in the 1970s put paid to this enjoyable lifestyle, forcing him to return to Wells. He found a job on a whelk boat and went bait-digging in the winter. Later he skippered the *Amethyst,* then the *Alison Christine.* In 1997, after twenty years involved with local boats, Allen became full-time coxswain/mechanic of the Wells lifeboat having served many years as a crew member. Allen said, 'In the lifeboat house you got a sense of history and pride. I wanted to be part of it.' He compared the old lifeboat with the modern one they now take pride in. 'You got soaked to the skin in the old open boat before you left harbour, but in the new one we have a decked-in wheelhouse. The new navigation aids have their uses, but I still use my compass and watch, just to double check.'

When I was invited to the Wells lifeboat house to talk to Allen about the weather, I saw history repeating itself. His teenage son was there, waiting to go bait-digging with his father when his duties at the lifeboat station had been completed. The lifeboat house was a joy to see, immaculate, shining and spotless, full of pride. Allen was completing his check of the first-aid kit carried on the boat. He took me upstairs to the lookout room. It was a bright sunny day, and before me stretched an unforgettable view. In the February sunshine the golden sands glistened wetly and the sand dunes curving out to a calm blue sea were empty and endless.

'The old boys got it mostly right,' said Allen. 'Of course there were no forecasts in those days. I don't always take too much notice of them myself, but I always look at the barometer and study the isobar charts.' The shipping forecast that dawn had given north-west winds, six to seven in strength with wintry showers. Allen commented 'The frost may have killed off the wind inshore, but the wind is laying off.' He pointed out to sea, to the Fall, a sandbank offshore, where there was a belt of clouds on the horizon. 'That's where the wind is. See the swells out there?' Allen pointed out the 'loom' of cloud seaward, and said he expected fine weather with light north-east or

43

Allen Frary and son Mark go bait-digging

east winds all day; the settled weather would last a day or two longer, as the ridge of high pressure was well established.

'I call this loomy weather. I always go by east hills. If they are bright and close and seem on top of you so that you can distinguish every sort of bush and tree, you can expect good settled weather. Normally you expect this with winds from the north round to the east. Then as the winds go into the south you can get mucky weather, hazy and foggy.' I was told after a flat calm day and an oily-looking sea, with a greasy sheen on it, one could expect wind; also a coppery colour in the sky indicated wind approaching.

Continuing the subject of wind, Allen told me that the westerly wind always went to bed with the sun, and that northerly gales never came up on spring tides, but that gales always came up on making tides and that the phases of the moon had a lot to do with winds backing or veering. 'We rarely get a flood tide in a north-east wind,' continued Allen, 'it'll make a bit more than it should, but not as much as in a direct north or north-west wind.'

The fishermen seem to find that if the wind was north or north-west with the ebb tide against the wind, when the flood started, the swell would come in and the crabs would run heavier coming out of the ground, and start feeding again. 'We always try to slip out and bait up the pots before a northerly swell comes in; then we can expect a good catch. I'm sure in a northerly swell the water agitates the crabs and they want to be going after something. Normally crabs are found in the bottom of the pot, but in a north-east swell they are invariably found in the top of the pots, trying to screw themselves out.'

Allen told me that the worst weather they got locally was a 'creeping breeze', normally experienced in south or south-west winds. 'The further off you go, you lose the lee of the land, then you're running before it; you don't notice the effect until you are off the Bellman (Blakeney Overfalls buoy), seven to eight miles from home. Then you have to decide whether to stay out and stick it out, or turn for home. That's the hardest one to judge, especially when you are many miles out.'

'Easterly winds are also hard to forecast on this coast,' said Allen. 'Normally a shore breeze will increase as the land heats up - but the worst conditions of all to be out in is fog. I'd rather have wind than fog any day. We have to go so far out when working these types of harbours; you have to use the tides and the wind, and judgement has to be on the point of no return. If you decide to go on, you're out for the day. You sometimes get a feeling, but you don't know what or why, that tells you whether you should go on or turn back.'

I asked Allen if he could ever remember getting the weather wrong. He thought for a bit then described one fishing trip when he and Tony (Jordan) went out in a drizzle. It cleared, then a strong northerly came in which they hadn't expected. He and Tony were able to haul only four shanks of pots each (they were working 40 pots to a shank, each pot weighing 22 lbs empty. 'It was uncomfortable!' said Allen, a master of understatement.

Allen talked about other weather signs. Gulls coming in at nights, to roost; if flying high in the sky, fine weather might be expected, but if they were flying in low, bad weather was on the way. This rule also applied to the flight patterns of swallows and swifts. If flight was low, the insects they were feeding on were also flying low, indicating dropping air pressure. Bad weather may also be expected if cats go crazy and chase their tails. When crabs crawl up to the top of the pots and hang on, that is a sure sign of wind coming up. Early morning, a fierce sunrise, 'like it will burn out your eyes' tells of wind on the way, whilst a gentle sunrise forecasts a fine day. A mackerel-backed sky forecasts rain. 'Rain before seven, clear by eleven' was nearly always accurate. A halo round the moon indicated wind or rain, as did a visible 'sun dog'. A slow gentle rise of the glass would mean fine weather, whilst the saying 'long foretold, long last' was rarely wrong. 'Postman's letters', little puffy clouds in the sky, foretold wind in the north or north-west.

Bait-digging was the next subject discussed. Spring tides were the worst for bait-digging, but on neap tides and in warmer weather, the worms were easier to get. A 'show' or worm cast was more difficult to detect in certain tides. After early morning tide, when one could dig six hours after high water, it was easy to see the casts, follow the line and get a good harvest. The best digging was on the early morning tide, but less good when the tides were afternoon ones. 'We hate those mid-morning and late tides, when tides are biggish; it takes a lot longer to get what you want,' said Allen. 'Early morning tides tend to be on the neap side, not such a flow of water off the sand; worms seem to prefer these conditions.'

Talking about working an open boat off the North Norfolk coast, Allen commented, 'Seas tend to run in a set of seven. You can't afford to make a mistake; you must always watch the sea. When there's a northerly swell in the water, the wind will always follow. When running into harbour in a swell, it's best not to look behind you, it'll frighten you.'

Whatever winds are blowing on the autumn equinox (September 21st), those winds will broadly continue from that quarter whilst the largest tides of the year continued, and even until the next equinox.

'The shipping forecasts have been often wrong for the last two to three years. If you listened to the forecasts you'd never go to sea,' concluded Allen.

I was reluctant to leave the lifeboat house and the company of such highly-skilled seamen. Walking back into the town, I thought how lucky the RNLI was to be able to call on the services of such articulate and experienced seamen and fishermen. Trained by their fathers to look at the weather and sea conditions until it became second nature, the quality of their judgements on weather conditions may save many lives at sea.

Andy Frary
Crab Fisherman, Bait-digger, Winter farm worker

Like his brother Martin, Andy grew up in Wells, went to the local school, finished his formal education at fifteen years, then continued his education in the big world of work.

'I always wanted to go to sea,' he explained. 'I'd only left school a week, and was fishing for whelks, when father came along the quay and said, "If you want a job, go and see Tony [Jordan]." So I went on my push-bike straight away and found Tony, and asked for a job. "Start on Monday" was Tony Jordan's reply.'

Years later Andy said 'Tony Jordan is the best seaman I ever did see, a marvellous seaman. One of the first trips I did with him was a rough trip. I can remember coming through the quay and Dad standing on the wall. Tony called up to him, "We broke him in now, he's had his first rough day and he knows what it was like".'

Andy said as a small boy he was always messing about in boats in the harbour. 'At one time the people from Lowestoft came to Wells in the bigger boats, the trawlers. I was desperate to get to sea, and the whelking job was then a dead man's job, because everybody had their own crew and you couldn't get on a boat for love nor money, so that was the only route to sea - but going with Tony set me up for life.'

Andy described two events that demonstrated Tony's skill in reading the sea. 'We all gathered on Wells Quay one morning, three hours after high water, and there was loads of water; nobody made a move, we all thought the weather was iffy. Then one boat made a move, so we all made a move, and Tony, against his better judgement, followed too, saying, "I don't think we'll haul our pots". There was a good south-easterly breeze but there was a northerly swell in the water, and the seas were leaping up and breaking together as we were going off. We got within six or seven miles of the pots and Tony, who was steering, started to turn the boat round. "You've seen something in the water?" I asked. "No," he replied, "we're going home, I don't like the look of this." Within fifteen minutes the breeze came in from the nor'west and the Wells lifeboat launched and came out for us all, and laid along the swell as we ran in, so if anything happened to any of the boats they could pick us up out of the swell.'

The second example demonstrating Jordan's amazing ability to

47

read the sea was in 1976-7. Andy described it as though it only happened yesterday.

'One day we were going off, and it was thick fog. There was no radar or GPS's, just pure, simple skill in observation. We got a diesel lock [block] in the engine and stopped to clear it. The fog got even thicker and we ran on a compass course. We hunted about for our pots, then Tony said, "We shall have to give up today, we've missed the gear." We started back in, and about five miles from Wells we saw some ripples in the water. "I know where I am now, I can see the ridge boiling up," exclaimed Tony. "We'll go back and haul the pots." So we turned round on to a five-mile north-easterly compass course through the fog, and the next thing we saw the buoys. Marvellous reading of the water; not many can do that as well as Jordan does.

'One time I thought I'd done wrong,' confessed Andy. 'We were going down the harbour one morning; there was a big flood tide and a big swell in the harbour. Father wanted some crabs, so we had to go. We got to the bottom of the harbour and we'd just about made it through, when this bloody great sea came up, really massive for our little open crab boat. "My God, what have I done?" I thought. As it came towards me it was rearing up all white, and just in the middle there was a bit of a V, so I headed the boat into it, and I got the speed of the boat just right and kept her straight or we'd have filled up and rolled over. Both me and my crew John, a fine seaman, got flung forward in the boat and saw water pouring into the boat like jets through the holes in the hull where the oars went. Our boat went up that sea and climbed over it and came down ready for the next one. We got away with it and father got his crabs that day.

'Another time we went out in lumpy conditions, it started to blow hard and it came through a westerly "nine". That's a lot of wind for a little twenty-foot boat. We got a couple of shanks of crabs before coming back. That day coastguards were keeping a watch. Father was panicking because he couldn't see us coming into harbour. Tony had always told me to keep well inshore, then work along the shore in these conditions, so I thought I'd try it. From Warham Hole, between Wells and Blakeney, the beach runs northwest-southeast, and we got in the lee of the beach all the way down the foreshore to the harbour. The coastguard couldn't see us but Tony said to father, "Don't

Martin and Andy Frary fishing for crabs

worry, he'll bring her along the shore like I taught him if he's got any sense.'"

Andy said the weather seemed to be tending, these last few years, to much greater extremes. 'You have to trust your own instinct. The sea will tell you a lot. On quite a calm day when there isn't a ripple on the water, yet on the side of the beach you'll get a little motion in the water, a tiny little swell; then you can expect the breeze to come in northerly.'

He commented on the changing fishing patterns. 'Whelking has nearly all gone now, just a couple go out from Wells. The ground has turned over to crabs. The seasons have changed without a doubt, sand and mud, or shallowing up. Before the '78 flood we caught a lot of whelks; we went back to the same grounds in the spring and the whelks had gone and there were tiny crabs all over the ground. Now whether that's because of the wind, or crabs from other areas settled in our grounds, we shall never know, but the crabs are established on these grounds now. If there's any whelk spawn the crabs will eat it. I am convinced that's why we no longer get any skate. The spawn is eaten by the crabs. They always say one thing takes over from another. I know a fisherman who goes for dogfish. I didn't realize the skill in hunting for dogfish; you "feel for them". Once you've found where they are, you shoot your lines, estimate how fast they are swimming and in which direction, but it's no good shooting your lines until you've made your calculated guess. Sometimes you shoot away for twenty fish, other times you get one hundred boxes. Years ago a fisherman told me that when there was a lot of calm weather the dogfish would laze about, not bothering to feed, but when they are swimming they are feeding, and you shoot your lines through them.

'You've also got to know where the crabs are going before you shoot your pots. When the winds are coming northerly the crabs are always in the roof of the pots. If you haul even in still weather and the crabs are in the roof of the pots you can depend upon it, the winds will be northerly next day. The crabs seem to know before we do of a change in the weather. In an easterly wind the crabs don't feed. In a backing wind you've got time to haul the pots, but when the wind is veering you haven't got time to complete the job. You can work with a south-westerly wind and go offshore, because once you have finished your job you know you're coming in to a fine harbour. When you go off in a nor'westerly you aren't going to do it because you know full well when you set out in good conditions, it will be blowing you into a "funny" harbour on your return. So it depends on the direction of the wind. You can work in a lot stronger south-westerly than you can in a northerly. It's not worth the risk coming into a harbour on this coast in the dark with a strong northerly. Summer is different from wintertime. The seas are far more heavy in the winter - density of the water. Tony Jordan used to say that when you hit a sea in the summer it's spray; when you get to wintertime and a lump of green water comes on board the sea is heavier. Roger Bishop, another fisherman who went with Tony, said the same thing. You've got more chance with a decked boat. You've got to be a far better seaman in an open boat. Father used to say, "Never think you're better than you are. The sea is always master."'

When asked if fishing was coming to the end of the run, due to changing weather patterns and more aggressive fishing techniques, Andy replied, 'I think there will always be fishermen, if you are prepared to work, but the money won't be there. But it's what you want to do with your life - enjoy the decision-making and freedom, or to be stuck in a building. Even today most fishermen work inland during the winter. I go sprout-cutting four months of the year. I can look up from the fields and see the sky or the light on the sea - marvellous, isn't it? The sad thing is that there aren't the youngsters coming on. You get the odd one interested in Wells, but most don't want the hassle or the hours. Most would rather travel into the towns and work a 9 a.m.-5 p.m. day. When I was young there were eight or nine of us desperate to get to sea.'

Asked whether he preferred crabbing or whelking, Andy replied, 'I don't really mind. I enjoy being at sea more than being ashore! It's a different environment out there. I've got to be outside; a house is a place to sleep in, and that's about it.

'It must be a godsend to have the fish stall on the quay,' I suggested.

'We'd always planned it that way. We've been fishing long enough to know that nothing lasts, whelking, sprats, shrimping, are all over-fished,' replied Andy. 'The bigger boats can go farther out and work deeper, and they can steam in so much quicker and avoid the bad weather, but a small boat like ours is more economical.'

Martin and Andy together have owned:
Black Beauty - open crab boat 19 ft 10 in length
Sarah Jane - open crab boat 22 ft length
Arandora Star - decked with wheelhouse 24 ft length

'People don't eat fresh fish like they used to,' said Andy. 'They want something out of a package. So my brother and I are wearing two hats, one as a fisherman and one as a salesman, and if we see a halo round the moon and know a wet weekend is coming up, we have to balance that with the catches we bring in. If we get a surplus of crabs you can keep them three or four days in a chiller; bad weather has the same effect on crabs as on humans. Bad weather dampens their activities. They go dormant in cold weather. So many people don't really care about the real fish like proper shellfish, mussels, and cockles these days. On the stall a big percentage ask for frozen processed fish like crab stix and prawn cakes.'

'Sea trout is a favourite of mine, they always come inshore when the weather is settled to clear off their sea lice and they come up on the shingle to clean themselves. You get a run of sea bass when bad weather is coming in.

'I can remember when I was a kid. Mother was born in Oakham

and Dad would take her three or four times a year to see the family. When we came back, Dad would go along to the quay to see the water, and say "Isn't it nice to be back! How lucky we are. We have a boat and we have the harbour and all that sand. This is worth a fortune."'

Now the next generation, Andy and Martin, has taken over, and Martin praised his brother's skill. 'One day the weather was deteriorating and we couldn't get in to the beach at Weybourne, so we went on to Wells. The bar was really bad and getting more dangerous while we watched, and there wasn't anywhere else to go, and there wasn't enough depth, but Andy brought the boat in on the back of a wave, and if she'd touched we'd have broached and broken up, but she didn't quite touch. It was a brilliant bit of judgement and seamanship in an open boat.'

The *Sarah Jane* with rain clouds looming

Martin Frary
Crab Fisherman

Most people who have visited Wells-next-the-Sea will have heard or know of Dennis Frary. For many years towards the end of his active days as a fisherman, he ran a popular shellfish stall on the quayside overlooking the creeks and salt marshes beyond the drying harbour. His cheerful greetings and friendly chatter as he and his wife served cockles, mussels, winkles and whelks to locals and holiday-makers made him a popular figure. Serving his country with distinction during the war, he returned to Wells in 1946 and started shell-fishing, following in his father's footsteps. Like *his* father, Dennis took his eldest son, Martin, cockling on the beach with him as soon as he could run about.

Martin, like his father Dennis, is smiling, ruddy of complexion, and full of energy. He and his brother Andrew are men who make a living as crab fishermen out of Wells. Their first crab boat was a small open boat, *Black Beauty*, some 19 ft in length, but as the crabs moved further north, the brothers needed a larger boat, the open 22 ft *Sarah Jane*. It sits proudly on its moorings in the harbour. Very recently the brothers have bought yet another boat, *Arandora Star,* 24 ft with a wheel house and decked in, and they have plans to fish further out as well as take fishing parties out from Wells. Martin said 'If you've got a good boat the job's easy, you're halfway there.'

Martin confessed to hating school and always wanted to follow the family tradition by earning his living from the sea. He says he enjoys his life as a bait-digger, wildfowler and crab fisherman. He has been fully occupied with these activities for over thirty years, but ruefully says, 'A family man could not make a living just from fishing these days. I go bait-digging in the winter and also do a bit of wildfowling.' Martin told me that when he was younger there was no money for fresh meat, instead they'd go on the marshes and get a goose, or a brace of rabbits or a hare. 'I've been out on the marshes since I was fifteen, and being a goose guide was a good source of income to supplement the fishing,' said Martin. He described how the 'old boys' (fishermen) took the gentry out on the marshes for the morning and evening flights and called the geese up. 'The geese would come in September time and would roost on the East Hills.'

'Pheasants won't fly into the sun,' said Martin, 'but they will fly on a dull day because they can see. Hares also cannot be driven into the sun.'

Depending on the weather, the Frary brothers go back to sea in March or April. 'It all depends on the weather; if it is too cold, we get nothing,' said Martin. 'There's no market for herring now; the modern man is not like us, he likes his fish pre-packed, and often pre-cooked.' Crabbing is their main occupation during the summer months, and I was told that the best bait for crabs was horse mackerel, but cod or any white fish would do the job. Tope was the best bait for whelks and little green gillies would be baited up to catch what few herrings were about.

Martin has four boys, but so far not one of them has expressed an interest in joining their father and uncle crabbing. Martin said he learnt all he knows about the sea and the weather from older men in the town. 'I first went out as a lad of fifteen with David (Cox). I'm fifty-three now, so had a lifetime at sea, and still I enjoy it. We had no navigation lights or life jackets in the early days, just a watch and a compass. We were often out there when we shouldn't have been - there were no reliable forecasts in those days. Once, my mate said, "I don't like the look of that weather," but I knew he'd been drinking, and I wanted to play football the following day, so I said, "Let's go; it doesn't look too bad," so we went!'

I asked Martin about weather warnings and was told that you always get a load of birds after the mackerel before a storm, because mackerel will feed up before bad weather and they are after whitebait. A blow, usually from the north, was on its way whenever they saw a shoal of mackerel feeding frantically. Another sign of bad weather, was to see the gulls flying round and round over the town.

'We're going to get a blow,' announced Andy, Martin's brother, one spring day when they were out hauling their crab pots. 'Oh, why's that?' asked Martin, and his brother said that all the crabs were hanging on to the top of the pots. Normally one expects to find the crabs in the bottom of the pots where the bait is. 'Sure enough,' said Martin, 'we got a gale from the north.' He told me that normally, whelks feed all the time, but crabs seem to feed up, then stop feeding, usually before the onset of bad weather.

I asked Martin about other weather signs. He replied, 'Very early one morning we were out steaming to our pots. The sun came up red and fiery, with angry red streaks right across the sky. We knew then we were in for some rough weather.'

When he was younger, the other fishermen warned him to look out for 'little postage stamps in the sky' - little fluffy white/grey broken clouds all over the sky. It was a sure sign of rain and wind. Another sign of approaching rain was when skylarks came straight out of the sky and hit the ground. Martin said he had often been bait-digging near the golf course when the skylarks would be high overhead, but if they dashed down to the ground that was a sure sign of impending rain. Another sure indication of approaching wind and stormy weather was to see the land suddenly become very clear. 'You could see the green of the coast for miles all around, and the land would look so close like it was rearing on top of you, and it invariably warned of wind coming in from the north or north-east.'

When he was still a youngster, the older men told the brothers that they'd never get any crabs until they saw frogs and toads crossing the road. The indicator was warmth. 'We never used to start crabbing until May, but now we start a month earlier in recent years. The weather is definitely warmer and so is the sea temperature. We don't get those bitter easterly winds for weeks on end like we used to. When my brother and I first started out, we'd fish the inner grounds in winter then go further out to the summer fishing grounds. Now, though, all this coast is fished out. Also we don't get the prolonged north-east winds that used to bring in the cockle and mussel spawn to come and set.'

I asked Martin to describe the worst weather he had ever experienced. With no hesitation he replied, 'We were out fishing in the Deeps. We had just hauled the pots when it began to snow and blow. We had two hours to wait before we could get back in harbour and by then it was blowing north-east force 8. In an open boat we wouldn't have stood a chance, but we were in the *Isobel Kathleen* and she's decked in. I've never seen the seas so bad; we couldn't find the harbour and we kept searchlights on the fairway buoy for two hours; we dare not leave her. Radar was no good, it was snowing too hard. We had to call up the lifeboat; by then it was blowing force nine. I had faith in the boat; she's the best boat round here for her size...she's a lovely boat.'

Martin said that as they left to fish that day, all the usual bad weather signs were there, fiery red sky, postage stamps everywhere and disturbed birds over the marshes. 'It was just a question of timing,' he said. 'Local weather gives us a lot to think about. I never go out without consulting the glass - it is more reliable than the weather they tell you about over the radio.'

Mardling with Martin was a tonic. These experienced fishermen know and love their boats, have vast experience of their bit of coast, and know if they get the weather wrong they have to live with their judgements. They are also masters of understatement, refreshingly honest, and brave seamen.

Martin Frary with his crab pots

Iain Hudson

'Between the Tides' Fisherman

Iain was born in 1946 in Burnham Thorpe. He now lives in North Creake. He calls himself a 'between the tides' fisherman. He says he learnt from the village people to look around him from a very early age, and terms himself a 'self-taught fisherman'. He went down to the shore with his father from the age of two, carried on the cross bar of his father's bike, getting a feed of winkles for tea. 'Cockles were a good feed when you had no money for meat,' he commented. When he was eleven, he would pick up winkles and go round selling them for 1s. 6d a pint. Leaving the local school at the age of fifteen, Iain first went to work at the Burnham Nursery. After one year he was sacked due to the 1963 big freeze up. He then went on the marshes and shot duck. 'We used to get up close to them behind the ice floes, but with the weather warming up we never see ice here now.' Iain worked on a coal cart for three years, and had a year in a bakery, before gladly returning to the land.

A countryman through and through, Iain's record of weather observations is extensive. 'After a galey day, you can expect an evening drop – that's when the heat of the land dominates. You always know when wind is coming in; there'll be a faint ripple on a calm sea, then you'll know the sea breeze is kicking in.' These were two things I learnt from him relating to local land and sea breezes.

Talking about cockling, Iain remarked that the morning tides would run, but the afternoon tides would not, so the fisherman, cockling on the beach, could expect the morning tide to ebb strongly, but the quarter tides, ones ebbing after midday, would not run. 'The birds would call up the tide. They knew when it was coming in and, anticipating a good feed, would start to holler.' Herring gulls would also warn of approaching bad weather, by flying inland.

Iain told me that when a sharp shower of rain was coming, the chickens would rush back to their hut or seek shelter, but if the rain was likely to be prolonged, they stayed outside. Bullocks would become uneasy before bad weather came in, and he always noticed that his cat would lie with its back to the fire when rain was on its way. Another sure sign of rain was when the cat washed right behind his ears.

'The marshes would stink when cows were on them and it was going to rain,' continued Iain, who then described 'mock suns' or 'sundogs', which also foretold approaching rain and stormy weather. 'Two fainter suns one either side of our own sun' was his description of them.

Iain owned a boat at one time, the *Miss Judith,* and by trailing a shrimp trawl behind he got a nice feed, but now prefers being a 'between the tides' fisherman. 'I go out after high water, and come in before it. I do a bit of longshore netting. You need a south-west wind to get results - anywhere off the land will do, otherwise you get too much roll. I do a cockle round, and I go samphiring in summer months. I know all the grounds of the Wash between Blakeney Point and the River Welland, and sometimes I get a few herring long-lining off Sheringham.' He said he would go out fishing all hours of day and night.

Iain pointed out that local weather patterns could not always be predicted nationally. 'We're high in North Norfolk,' he pointed out. 'If you get a thunderstorm, Hunstanton cliffs, being high, will split it. Lightning always tries to earth. Once I was off a beach and my face went numb. Luckily I had rubber boots on, because the lightning was trying to earth.'

Talking about the changing coastline, Iain said 'When I was fifteen, you could get a day's shooting at Scolt Head; there were acres of land. Now, due to erosion, all the hills have gone; half of Scolt Head now lies in Holkham Bay. Years ago,' said Iain, 'a man spent his days working on the beach putting in faggots to halt the erosion. Now nothing is done, and it is called "managed retreat."' He pointed out that the coast was sweeping westwards continually, and there was nothing to halt it. It was no good putting sea defences along the beach, because the sea would only undermine them; structures had to be put in at an angle to have any chance of delaying the erosion of the coastline of North Norfolk.

I asked Iain about fog, and was told that years ago fog was much more prevalent than in modern times. A fog in November could hang about three or four days in years gone by. Iain described how he once got lost in fog along a coastline he knew as well as the back of his hand. 'We were only thirty yards or so from Scolt Island, when I decided to turn back because I could feel the fog was getting denser. We came up in Holkham Bay into the Pine Belt. Once you are lost and turn, it is very difficult to keep on course,' was his casual description of one of the most frightening of weather phenomena.

Iain enjoys life on the marshes, wildfowling, and says his bag sometimes contains teal, wigeon, pink-footed geese, greylags and Canada geese.

Being a practical horticulturalist, Iain described how starfish dug into the allotment gave wonderful crops. Alternatively, if boiled and fed to rats or unwanted cats, the starfish meal would kill them off because it was quite indigestible. Bladderwort dug into the ground would help to provide a good crop of potatoes, because the seaweed never dried out, and would contain the dawn dews and provide constant moisture in the soil, which suited a potato crop ideally.

Wells Lifeboat rescuing a yacht off Blakeney Sands
The yacht is being pounded off Blakeney. The Lifeboat is in
attendance. Assessment of weather and sea conditions test the skill
of the Lifeboat coxswain (Alan Frary)

Anthony Jordan
Wells Lifeboat Coxswain, Fisherman, Sailor

Calling at Mr and Mrs Jordan's to see a wooden carving some three feet high, that Mr Jordan had dug out of the coastal sands off his fishing ground at Wells some twenty years ago, gave me a wider view of that enigmatic man. I had seen him in the town, a reserved, pipe-smoking, energetic man, always active and often seen in his familiar blue smock, busy outside the whelk sheds at East Quay. I had rarely spoken with him, but I greatly respected him. Walking into his cosy home, Tony, now retired from the sea, was cheerful and friendly. His house virtually smelt of sea breezes. Every wall and space was filled with beautiful pictures of the Wells lifeboat and crew, photographs of boats, unusual sea shells, and model boats in bottles. Framed and taking pride of place, were the certificates from the Lifeboat Institution, testifying to Tony's seamanship and bravery when he was a lifeboat man in the Wells-next-the-Sea lifeboat. His years of service were:-

Crew Member 1946-71
Second Coxswain 1971-86
Coxswain 1986-89

Retiring after forty-three years 'on call', he had helped save forty-one lives at sea. The certificate was awarded on June 24th 1989, when he received the B.E.M. at County Hall from the Lord Lieutenant of Norfolk.

Tony was second cox in 1979 when, in hurricane conditions, he and David Cox took a joint decision with their crew to launch the Oakley, a relatively small lifeboat from Wells station, to help a damaged ship in danger of breaking her back on the Dudgeon shoals. 'Some of the crew had had enough before we got halfway there, yet we all had another five hours' appalling weather in a severe gale,' remarked Tony, referring to that launch. 'There was no cover in that open boat, just a little windscreen. After that launch, every Oakley lifeboat around the coast had a canopy built around her. When I got home after that trip, my missus ran me a hot bath and put a quarter tin of mustard in, and I was alright and glowing again.'

Tony said he always watched the glass; the barometer was the best weather indicator ever invented. 'There used to be a barometer on Wells Quayside; everybody looked at it. It was situated outside Styman's shop; previous to that, it was up against the old harbour wall. It was a beautiful instrument. There was no other means of getting forecasts in the early days, we just relied on our knowledge and experience. When I first went to sea, you never got a forecast, there was nothing on the radio.'

Tony first went to sea just before the war ended, around 1944. 'I was fourteen, and I went with old Cyril "Gully" Grimes, our boat was small and we used to go a long way off. Gully was the son of Billy Grimes who for many years was coxswain of the *Baltic*. She was the last pulling and sailing lifeboat Wells had. She went off station in 1936. We had the last horse-drawn launching carriage here as well.'

Tony had always wanted to go to sea, but on his first trip, although it was like a millpond, he was so seasick and bad, even before they left the harbour, that he became almost unconscious. It was eighteen months before he got over the symptoms, but since it was the only job he wanted to do, he stuck it out.

'What was it like in the early days?' I asked. 'You were fishing in a small boat out of a drying harbour, with no reliable weather forecasts.'

'There were tons of everything,' was Tony's immediate reply. 'There were tons of whelks; you could lay lines anywhere and catch good-sized fish without going all the miles we have to go now. In wintertime we'd work off Blakeney Deeps, and in spring we'd just jump over the Falls, and gradually work all the way off - anything up to 2½-3 hours as we used to steam. We all used sails in those days, dipping lug, canvas sails; if we got a fair wind, we'd sail all the time.' Tony told me that in those early days the fishermen would all weigh up the weather as the morning sun rose, take a note of sun dogs, and judge whether the sky looked a bit greasy and blotchy, with a miniature rainbow. 'That would be a sure sign of wind and rain,' he said. 'It might take 24-30 hours before it arrived, so we had to judge whether we could use the weather before it turned bad.' I was interested in Tony's next remark, 'In the morning sky you'd see "postmen", little white clouds scudding across the sky, always a sign of a breeze. A "mackerel-backed" sky always meant a change in the weather, but if the clouds were really high first thing in the morning, winter or summer, you'd be sure of fine weather for six or seven hours.

'A lot of the time you can't take notice of the forecasts they give you, even local ones,' maintained Tony. 'The areas are so vast - even, say, between Humber and Thames. They might forecast a gale, but if you were lying in the centre of the depression, you'd get no wind at all. I've been to sea many a time when they gave out a bad forecast, and we had a beautiful day. Also it depends on whether they give a backing or veering wind. On this coast if it's backing, say from south-west backing to southerly or south-easterly, you can depend you'll get that breeze within five or six hours, then it'll be through. Normally it would come through on the ebb tide, then it'll freshen and start blowing a backing wind. If they gave a north or north-east wind, we'd all go down and read the water. In this area consider the distance you have to go before you get any shelter from the land in a northerly.'

Tony informed me that in the early days they always went away on the ebb tide, but if a swell was making (increasing) on the ebb, they put the tiller over and went home because they knew they would have no time to get their pots in. 'Swell as a rule makes on the flood,' said Tony, 'it will always come on the beach in the full flood, that's the way it works. In the first hour of the flood tide, the tide would always be the roughest and the swell would also be the worst then. The sea can tell us fishermen more than the wind does, and the seas here change so quick. It can be flat calm and within an hour you'll see a lift and you'll know something's coming in. The beach men would always try to come ashore before the flood tide because that's when the swell came in, then they'd have trouble getting ashore.'

Tony continued, 'I always took notice of what the old 'uns told me; then you would weigh up the rest on your own. The sea will tell you a lot. You can go down in an east wind and there'll be all the swell you wanted, then another hour off and the sea is different again. You can normally tell by how the swell is coming at you; if it's got a lot of velocity behind it, you know you're in for a good breeze.'

Tony said he learnt to sail by just 'picking it up'. He raced at Norwich Frostbites S.C. and belonged to the Wells S.C., often crewing an International 12 sq metre Sharpie.

After fifty years at sea Tony was glad to finish his job; he now enjoys his grandchildren. He is sure the weather is changing. 'There is so much more rain and wind. Years ago the patterns were so much different. They used to say "Rain before seven, clear by eleven - rain after eleven, last all day." You can' go on that now. The weather patterns baffle a lot of people these days. In the old days when you were at sea, you could weigh the situation up, and know what was coming. I've not been caught out many times. I used to be known for going out when the weather was bad, bull-headed, but I never had the lifeboat after me, although it did launch one day when I was out. I had my son with me, and John Dickinson, and we had no radio in the boat – no one had radio in their boats in those days. All the other boats came back and I hauled our pots seven miles out, then went on to get the other gear twelve miles on. The coastguard was keeping an eye out for us and didn't know I'd gone on and thought we'd foundered. We were on our way in - there was a gale from the west – and when we were six miles off the beach, we saw the lifeboat. I was second cox'n then, so said to my crew "I guess lifeboat's got a shout and they need me," but I soon realised they'd come out for us. I said to David, "Who are you after?" and he said, "You".

'Several times we've all been out and had to make a run for it and the lifeboat has come to escort us all into harbour - just come through a fresh breeze that lasted 10-12 hours and we've gone back to sea next day! Some of the old boys would never go more than 9-10 miles out in any weather. It was up to the individuals, some would come home with a lot more stuff if they went further out. We were totally reliant on what we caught to keep the rat from the door. I often used to be out and the weather was bad, but I'd stop and haul a couple of shanks aboard to get some weight in the boat, to get her head down in the water, then shoot them closer to the shore where it wasn't so rough, to pick up next day; with a bit of weight your boat is more stable.'

'When you came home, if there was a swell on the make, you knew damned well you'd not be at sea next day - you always knew what it would be like next day.'

'It's a bad sign as a rule if you can see lights a long way off - if you could see all the buoys flashing - especially if you went away in the dark. Once I was off with old Loady. We had only gone to the back of Blakeney Overfalls ground, and he said, "Put the tiller hard over, we're going home, that Cromer Light's so brilliant we're going home!' Old Loady could weigh up the weather, and he knew if visibility was that good over 20 miles, and all the navigation buoys in the area were twinkling all round the horizon with a fresh breeze, it meant bad weather on the way.

Recovering the Wells lifeboat

David Cox joined us and he and Tony visibly relaxed and talked easily together. Tony said to David, 'Did you tell them about your grandfather, with the weather breezes?' Then the two men explained, 'Like this time of year [February], you can get a nice fine day, sun shining, "mirrors on the water" we'd call it, silhouettes of all the boats reflected in the water. "Another weather breeze, you won't get there tomorrow," one said, and he was nearly always right. Loady used to say on a fine day such as we're talking about, if you saw little old gnats flying, he'd say, "That's a bad sign!" Same with seagulls when they come in nights, if they come in straight you've got a fine day next, but if they come in and circle, turn and twirl over town you can bet your life you've got a gale of wind coming. Same with birds going up to roost, if they go in threes and go up to the top of a tree, it's going to be fine, but if they're well down the tree, you know it's going to blow and rain. If crows build high in the trees you can reckon on a good summer. Old Basil, a gamekeeper, he had partridges and you can weigh the weather with them. The same with bantams, if it's going to be fine they'll be up in the top of the trees and sit there with the old pheasants and pigeons, but if the weather's going to deteriorate, they'll be halfway down the tree and right down on the lowest branches.'

Tony and David continued to reminisce. 'When we were out whelking in winter and had had a fine spell then you'd see all the whelks trying to burrow out of the bottom of the pot; if they were curled up under the crinnie [net round the top of the pot to prevent escape] it invariably meant "in for a breeze," which meant a gale of wind from the north-east and a big swell. If you were out all week and got good pots of whelks and then one day a lot of crabs, it showed we were in for swells, and the pots "wouldn't fish"; you'd get instead a lot of old gillies. When you see a lot of old gillies [harbour crabs, known by differing names along this coast, *swinners* at Brancaster, *Tom Cads* at Cromer and Sheringham] nip up early in the year you'd know you were in for a hard winter.

'Years gone by you put out a few old gillie pots on the quay to get bait for the whelks, but we never saw gillies in the winter; they lay up. Gillies are on the move all the year round, but years ago they'd bury up in the mud when it got cold. Weather is changing. They're catching crabs now [February]; years ago you wouldn't see a crab winter time, they'd all be holed up. In Sheringham years ago they'd want the temperatures to reach 46°F before they'd put the crab pots out and if you got an east swell in the water, everything would go dormant. They got more east winds then than we do now. Years ago you got east winds right up till June or until the longest day, then it would change. One year we couldn't haul our pots in for seven weeks because of east winds.'

'When we used to go hare shooting, we'd go across ploughed fields frozen like iron even in March. You don't get such hard frosts nowadays. In old times summer used to have long-term fine spells with moderate west breezes in the morning. It would keep veering round and until it got round to north to east, then freshen during the afternoon, then die in the evening, and it would be west again next day. In those conditions you could get a fine spell for weeks. Whilst winds go clockwise you're in for a fine spell.'

'As regards fishing, years ago we went to sea and would work a couple hundred whelk pots, no more, and got a good livelihood; now people are too greedy. Now there is no hard work like we had; modern boats have got hydraulic gear and big closed-in boats - now the industry is overfished in every area.'

David and Tony stopped mardling, and I felt privileged to have listened in to these professional seamen and fishermen, who knew their boats and the feel of the sea and the wind.

Tony concluded, 'We often used to come home all the way in the dark without looking at the compass, just used the wind and the motion of the boat to tell us where to go.' Night time they frequently steered by the heavenly bodies. One of Tony's ex-crew, George Jay (a very humorous man who crewed Jack Cox fishing), one night said 'I've passed that star, where do I go next?'

In the age when Tony and David went to sea for a living, they did not have the advantage of modern gear and clothing; if they got wet as they crossed the bar, they stayed wet all day. Together David Cox as cox'n and Tony as second cox took the Wells lifeboat to sea in February in hurricane-force winds, probably the worst conditions ever experienced by such a small lifeboat on this coast (it was too bad for the Coltishall helicopters to take off). Such bravery, seamanship and understanding of the sea conditions and the weather must teach future generations how to look at weather with new eyes.

Toughness, too, was another attribute these fine seamen took for granted. Talking with Tony's daughter one day, I was told of an accident at sea. 'In the 1970's Dad's face was hit by a fouled anchor swinging off the hauler as they recovered tangled pots. It hit him on

66

the head and threw him 12 feet into the bow of the boat. He just had time to tell the two boys the course to steer, after he had radioed for help and given his position, then lost consciousness. He was airlifted off the boat with a fractured jaw and several hairline fractures of his skull and suffering from hypothermia. Even today, some thirty years on, he has pain in his face and loose teeth. Dr Hoddy [the local doctor] went out in the helicopter and was dipped in three times, so he also had a bad time of it,' said Margaret with a warm smile of appreciation.

The *William Edward* (foreground) and the *Sally* alongside.

Fishermen's boats mean a lot to them. Tony said 'I started whelk-fishing at the age of fourteen in May 1945 with Cyril Grimes, my stepfather. The first boat I sailed on was motor/sail *Rose* LN76, length 26 feet beam 10 feet. The full dipping lugsail was in continuous use. *Rose* was built at Sheringham in 1936 by R. E. Emery & Sons. She was sold in 1950.'

'Next I sailed on motor/sailor *William Edward,* length 30 feet, beam 11 feet; she had a dipping lug LN 8 and was built in April 1949 by R. E. Emery & Sons. She was a family boat for 47 years and her sails were used for 35 years of her working life.'

'For about 20 years we had two boats in the firm. We also had motor/sailor *Sally* LN 141, length 28 feet, beam 10 feet 6". I was skipper of her all the time we owned her.'

Bygones Video made in 1987 by Dick Joice
'Tony Jordan'

This makes all other jobs seem soft.

In the *William Edward,* a 1949 open sailing boat, Tony learnt to become a fisherman and a seaman. It was the oldest boat in the fleet operating out of Wells-next-the-Sea, a charming, working fishing town, with about fifty pubs in 1903, and a fleet of dark brown canvas sailing work-boats. Whelking, crabbing, long-lining and bait-digging were the main occupations for the men supporting large families in the town.

Tony learnt to become a whelk fisherman. The routine was to steam for three hours to reach their fishing grounds, haul their pots, then steam home another three hours. One needed a ton and a half a day to make it pay. There were thirty-six to forty pots in a fleet or shank, and a crew of three men to work the boat. In those days (1950s) there were five boats and crew in Wells; now in 2001 there is only one. Alan Cooper is the last full-time whelk fisherman from Wells. Each man in the boat had his own specific job. The first hauled the pot, the second riddled and emptied each pot, and bagged up the whelks, whilst the third man baited up the pot (salt herring was the preferred bait) for the next day's catch.

When Tony started at the age of fourteen years, there were no electric winches, no electric lights, and not even a thermos flask in which to carry hot drinks. Tony used to have a bottle of cold tea. The whelking pots were made of a heavy cast-iron base, with tarred cord tightly wrapped around the frame. Nowadays, they are lighter, being constructed of plastic-covered wire. The first boat Tony worked on was a dipping lug sailing boat; the sail was made of heavy brown canvas, 280 square feet in size. In more modern times, the mast and

68

sails were removed to make room for the more modern gear such as VHF, radar and radio equipment.

'All I ever wanted to do was to be a fisherman,' explained Tony; 'when my son Stephen was fifteen, he came with me after he left school.'

During the war, the Wells whelkers fished to feed the nation. During the mid-1960s 9,000 tons were landed annually. Whelks are a common maritime snail, and after being boiled or steamed in the whelksheds at East Quay, Wells, they were bagged up and sold locally and far a-field for five pounds a full bag, and during the summer months the Wells whelkers aimed to fish daily, weather permitting, visiting their pots daily.

Now the whelks are gone. The film showed a nostalgic view of these resourceful fishermen, and their amazing long hours and hard work to bring back to port a mollusc, which is a scavenger of the sea bed. The film of the fleet of boats coming over the bar on a rising tide, unloading their catch into small boats to be taken into the whelk sheds where boiling coppers were ready and waiting, made magnificent film of a now almost extinct way of life.

Ray Smith
Retired seaman

Ray Smith is a retired seaman living in Wells. He was born there in 1935 and spent his early years in Wells and the neighbouring village of Warham. There was a village school in Warham in those days and he won a scholarship from there to the local grammar school at Fakenham.

Ray's family had all been in service for several generations, mainly at Holkham Hall where his father began his working life at the age of fourteen as Steward's Room boy in the kitchen, following *his* father, who began in the same job thirty years before.

As Ray grew up amongst his family, he was taught to catch, prepare and cook food in the old ways of country people, and absorbed the knowledge and manners of servants and how to understand and appreciate the quality and style of good living which set the tone for the rest of his life.

This was apparent when we had dinner with him one evening. He cooked us a six-pound sea trout he had caught himself that morning on Wells beach, served with fresh shellfish, and vegetables from local gardens, beautifully prepared and accompanied by excellent wines, obviously chosen by someone taught to love the table from his earliest years.

Over dinner his conversation was filled with an unusual mixture of the poetic and practical, memories of all the childhood interests of the country boy who was lucky enough in those days to have the freedom to indulge them. He had a passion for boats and fishing, and, mad about birds, he had a collection of birds' eggs running to over a hundred species.

From his earliest years he recalled the excitement of his first catches, his first trout from the river Stiffkey at Warham as an eight-year-old, and running straight home to mother to have it cooked immediately. At the same age he caught his first hare in a snare, secretly carried home to his grandmother's, terrified of meeting the gamekeeper; the old lady, who had spent her working life in kitchens of stately homes, cooking for everyone from the king downwards, showed the boy how to prepare 'jugged' hare.

He recalled all the pleasures of childhood fifty years ago, catching eels with a 'fyke' net or a long-handled 'glave' or 'peyke' or eel 'babs' (worms threaded on to woollen lines); mackerel 'railing', 'kipping' lines for flat fish, or walking the shallows in the creeks with a 'butt' fork; catching shrimps, prawns and whitebait, gathering cockles, winkles and mussels, and digging clams in the mud banks, and in their season gathering samphire and gulls' eggs. Looking back on his childhood he regrets that all this is no longer part of a modern child's life, so much of it has been lost.

His father took him to sea one day when he was 11 years old in an old-fashioned Wells open whelk boat, the *Rose*, with Gully and Rowley Grimes and young Tony Jordan. From that day on his only interest was the sea and his ambition was to get away as soon as he could. The local Sea Scout troop was his great love and paved the way for sea school; the local vicar-cum-schoolmaster secured him a place and he was off to sea at 16.

His first trip to sea was on an Orient line, the *Orontes*, as a deck boy, where he learned to scrub and polish and make tea, and he remembered the thrill when the quartermaster of his watch taught him how to steer this huge ship.

He moved on to tramp steamers, got a taste for travel and learned to use ships to explore. In the fifties, jobs were easy to come by, and he would go to the Pool, the seaman's labour exchange, to see what was going and take his pick.

Canada was one of his favourite countries and he spent his first few years at sea working out of eastern Canada down to America, Australia and New Zealand, with many trips across the Atlantic. The fifties was a good time to be at sea, so much trade and so many ships, full of interest for a boy. He loved to watch the last of the old sailing craft, particularly the schooners on the Newfoundland Banks, often passing lonely fishermen working their longlines for cod from a dory, miles from land. There was always a sight to see from his turn on lookout, sometimes from a crow's nest, high up the foremast; watching for ice in fog would keep him alert. The old hands would tell him 'You can smell the fog'. 'And so you could,' said Ray. 'Suddenly the air would be colder and clammy and the fog would come from nowhere.'

As a boy, he was fascinated by the talk of old men, many of whom had served in sail, and he loved their yarns and wild stories, and regretted that he had missed sailing in 'square riggers'.

Weather lore was a favourite topic of conversation, full of tall stories, superstition and peculiar rhymes that had to be explained to the boy:-

'When the rain's before the wind,
Then your sheets and halyards mind.
When the wind's before the rain,
Soon you may make sail again.'

First rise after low
Then expect a stronger blow.

Perfectly straightforward. Some of them made good sense, even though they remained a mystery to the outsider:-

'Mackerel sky and mares' tails,
Make tall ships carry low sails.'

Translated into everyday speech this means that clouds blown out by high altitude winds, altocumulus into a dappled pattern resembling the marking on a mackerel's back, and altocirrus blown into ragged wisps resembling mares' tails were a sign of high altitude winds which might soon appear at sea level, forcing the sailing ship to take on her topmast sails and run under the low sails of storm rig.

As a seaman he learned to have a constant awareness of the weather and to watch it continuously.

All the details of the wind, sea and temperature, and above all the barometer, would be entered in the ship's log at the end of each four-hour watch.

The barometer was the great pointer for all forecasters and was always given special attention by the watch-keeper as he kept his weather eye open, frequently looking into the eye of the wind to see what was coming.

Always be aware that once you are out to sea and out of reach of shelter you have no choice but to make the best of things. 'Hope for the best, but prepare for the worst - and quite often the worst is what you get,' said Ray philosophically.

In the early 60s Ray described how he came back from a deep sea job on an Everard boat. They had Decca navigation on the ship, and he fancied himself as a posh navigator. He was with an old Norfolk skipper, going along the coast, and when they passed a lighthouse Ray took a vertical angle with a sextant. The Norfolk skipper remarked,

'Boy, you can't be much bloody good if you need to use one of them things along the coast.'

Coming back from his last trip to return to land to take his master's certificate, he went to a local dance, met a girl, fell in love and, after seventeen years at sea, 'swallowed the anchor' at the age of thirty-two.

The hard work took its toll; Ray spent three months in hospital with a massive hernia, so maybe his present love of the sea as a hobby, fishing off the coast for local sea trout and mullet in a local boat, is the best compromise for him. He had been due for a ship of his own, having served as master on several trips, but now finds his love of the sea satisfied in local trips off Wells. 'Some days, out there just for fun is sheer bliss. To drift round all day, you don't have to catch fish, it is enough to just be there. Perhaps it is just as well all the fish have gone - I sometimes wonder how all the local fishermen make a living. Just occasionally we still get good sea trout and some wonderful bass, but after two seals have lived in Wells harbour for some days, there is very little left to catch.'

'Once I had a wonderful season on an Everard's boat up in Norway; we got beautiful cod. One day we caught a 20 lb halibut. We cooked it the same day and ate the lot - wonderful eating. I suppose that was where I got my love of cooking and appreciation of good food.'

'Professional seamen don't get on too well with yachtsmen, particularly those that play with the sea in expensive yachts and plastic motor boats.' Ray spoke with scorn of the 'yachties' who have no idea of the realities of the sea. To the professional seamen it could be a life of incredible drudgery and monotony, when the ship became a prison, and you had to serve out the sentence and do the best you could.

Cyril Southerland

Crab, Whelk, Mussel, Oyster Fisherman

Mr and Mrs Southerland live in a cottage at Brancaster Staithe. The view from their kitchen window is one to die for. The day we called, the tide was ebbing, and the blue sky hung over the green marshes as far as the eye could see. The skyline was low; no other buildings obstructed the sea view; the well-tended vegetable garden and greenhouse leading from the house down to the marshes, was highly productive.

Cyril, born at the end of the war, in 1945, grew up in the house we now visited. It had belonged to his grandparents, and quite recently the Southerlands have extensively renovated the family home. In the sitting room prominent pictures of Cyril's children taken on their degree days in cap and gown, proudly pronounce that the family have all done well in further education.

Cyril's father and grandfather on both sides were fishermen, making a living from harvesting local cockles, whelks and mussels. One grandfather owned an oyster smack and dredged for oysters, and the other was one of the first to fish for whelks from Brancaster.

Cyril was called 'the lodger' by his family because, when the children were growing up, he worked such long hours at sea, six days a week. 'Sunday was a day for the family,' recalled Cyril with a happy smile. These days Cyril runs a retail business and his card pronounces him a 'Shellfish Merchant'. He firmly believes in conservation of fish stocks. 'I catch a few crabs and take quality mussels and oysters to the local hotels. I do not use a dredge on the lays but work by hand, so the quality is kept up.'

The harbour has been good to his family of fishermen. 'There were always mussels and oysters in the winter and whelks and cockles in the summer. As a boy I always dreamed of going to sea, but it was not a straightforward choice. As a ten-year-old boy I caddied all weekends on the Royal West Norfolk golf course at 5 shillings a round and went to work at a local butcher's five nights a week and often all day Saturday. There were four in the family so things were tight. I detested the butchery; they were good to me, and treated me like a son, but my heart wasn't in the trade, so at sixteen years I went to work at the local garage, and after a couple of years I knew I didn't

74

want to spend my life there either. That winter there was a wonderful set of mussels came into the lower harbour and my father said, "Boy, you'd better leave the garage. You won't be happy till you get down them creeks." So my father and I had a good winter with mussels. We worked together and I still lived at home. We had small mussel boats, the 15-foot locally-built Brancaster "mussel flat". After three or four years mussel and cockle fishing, I could see the potential in whelk fishing which my uncles were engaged in. Gaining experience by bringing in mussels and cockles from the Wash into our Brancaster beds, I learnt about tides and weather by working with another fisherman.'

The Southerland family's undecked fishing boat

Cyril's cousin and uncle had a new boat built, so Cyril bought his uncle's whelk boat, a 30-foot Hoveller built at King's Lynn in 1948 with a basic petrol engine. Cyril learnt the hard way, finding his gear by pocket watch and compass, just as the old fishermen had done for centuries. He roped his own whelk pots, and for the next few years continued whelk fishing in the Race Channel some 10-12 miles off the Norfolk coast, north-east of Brancaster.

Some three years on, Cyril's other uncle retired and Cyril took

75

over this boat, and this being a decked boat they were able to follow the whelks further a-field.

In the 70s there were some hot summers and mild winters and this resulted in a decline in the whelk stocks. At the same time a huge number of crabs came in. In 1975, during the hot summer, Cyril remembers his whelk pots became full of small edible crabs and the whelk spawn was eaten by the crabs. Soon followed a complete decline in whelk fishing in that area but crab fishing took over.

'The Wash is a very interesting place to work in,' commented Cyril. 'You go along in twenty to thirty feet of water, then suddenly you go into about five feet. You can't ignore the tides or the wind or the waves. If you get a north or a south wind in the Wash they can be bad winds because they are either with or against the tide.'

Location is all-important in the Wash. Cyril explained, 'When we went across to Boston, we would leave at high water; if the winds were west or south-west you'd get past Hunstanton, and the seas would be so steep and the motion over Sunk Sand so violent you'd think you should turn back, but a few miles on under the shelter of the Lincolnshire side, past Buoy No. 1, then the seas would flatten out and the day would be fine.'

Cyril said he admired the old Lynn fishermen in the days when they went fishing in sailing boats and the oyster smacks; deep draught boats in the shallows of the shifting sand banks meant they had to watch and read the waves and weather continuously.

Climate, conditions and local weather play a large part in conserving fish stocks. Cyril said that the recent cold weather (2000) had produced a good spat of mussels, but the more recent warmer conditions generally had resulted in lower stocks of mussels to be had. A cold winter generally encouraged the mussels to spawn.

At the end of the 1980s when it was not economic to continue whelk-fishing Cyril adapted his career at sea to mussel and oyster cultivation, collecting the seed mussels from the Wash, growing them on in his beds and working them out during the winter; also cultivating oyster stocks.

As well as earning his living with mussels and oysters, Cyril decided to go crabbing. Four to five years of this occupation gave Cyril a living, but then he returned to the mussels, deciding that the market for mussels and oysters was expanding, but dressing out a small number of crabs and supplying the local hotels gave him a good summer living.

Grading whelks by machine in the big freeze of 1987

small number of crabs and supplying the local hotels gave him a good summer living.

For over a hundred and twenty years fishing has gone in cycles. 'When one door closes, another opens,' observed Cyril and the weather patterns are largely responsible for these variations. Climatic conditions are mainly responsible for any species spawning in the sea. During the very cold spell in the winter of 1962-63 when ice floes were in the Brancaster creeks, and froze them for weeks on end, all fishing came to a standstill, but the following hot summer, the creeks were full of cockle and mussel spat. Through the 60s and 70s, times were good for the fishing industry, which coincided with Cyril's best time in the trade, whereas the very hot summer of 1975, combined with the mild winters of 1974 and 1975, coincided with a massive spat of crabs, which may have been responsible for the decline in the local whelk fishing in the 1980s.

Radar only came into Cyril's life in 1975. He remembers that in his early days of using radar, they used to hang polythene bags on their pots so that the bleep would identify the position. 'Radar was really good for fog,' Cyril recalled. 'In the Race Channel, being run down was always in your mind and in fog, just a pocket watch and a compass was little help with the busy shipping lanes with supply vessels for the gas platforms increasing in numbers. Radar took a lot

77

of anxiety out of the job, especially when coming back on to harbour; the wreck, foreshore, and the clubhouse came up, even in the dark and in fog. It was a real boon.'

'Whelking could be done every day in my time; the trade was there, but the weather was always the deciding factor and you took a risk to go out when the demand for whelks was so high.'

'Weather forecasting is an art, not a science, and every day we would worry, "Can we get there, can we haul our pots, and get back, and is the risk worthwhile?" Our grandfathers were brought up with the barometer - that was all they would talk about. "Is the glass up?" they would worry. "Is it standing on its head?"'

Cyril said that in his early days of fishing, his father and uncles would watch the barometer continuously, knowing that if the glass was steady, there might be a breeze, but fishing would be practical, whereas if the glass was very low, that was a time when you shouldn't take a chance because, probably, you were in the eye of a low pressure system. An old saying, 'The quicker it fall, the quicker it rise,' told them of stormy weather ahead, even gale force winds on the way.

Cyril recalled the time when, about 04.00 hours, his uncle commented 'I don't think I'm going today - the glass is standing on its head.' Several boats went out, because there wasn't a breath of wind, yet by 08.30 hours a north-west gale was raging and Wells lifeboat was launched to help the whelk fishing boats that got caught out. A pleasure boat, a 27-foot naval cutter, was out tope fishing. The fishermen beached it on Scolt Head and it got completely smashed up. Another boat took some holidaymakers out whelk-fishing, and when the gale sprang up so unexpectedly, the sails were taken off the boat to wrap round the engine box to protect it from the waves, as they were on the pump continuously, and one of the party commented, "I expect you often go out in weather like this"!'

'The old 'uns would notice a quick drop of the glass and note a quick deterioration in the weather, but a slow fall of pressure would indicate weather was going to deteriorate gradually. A quick rising glass indicated wind was on the way.'

Cyril also said that the old ones were marvellous at judging weather, but when T.V. came in they weren't so good, because they took too much notice of the forecasts on the screen. Cyril said for himself he had got used to reading the T.V. weather, especially taking

78

note of the highs and the lows. His principle, apart from being aware of the barometer readings, was to note the position of the highs and lows on the screen and try to read how they were going to develop. 'Tides also have a lot to do with the weather,' he said. 'For the big tides, storm tides, you have to look what's happening to the weather in Scotland, to see where the low pressure is going. The north-west wind in Scotland, coming down the North Sea, can have a lot of effect in East Anglia. How strong the ebb tide is, is also a good indicator of weather brewing up.'

Cyril recalled that when working at sea hauling for whelks, the custom was to drop down with the tide, and the strength of the ebb tide going round the British Isles to the north-west was the big indicator of weather ahead. Judging how strong the ebb tide was, would tell them what to expect. He recalled once, when they were hauling and dropping down to the north-west, a sudden ground swell sprang up and there was no noticeable ebb; a gale of wind to the north in Scotland was on its way down the North Sea and the swell was four to five hours ahead of the wind.

Learning to read the sea, said Cyril, was a continuous process. They usually hauled pots at low water, and he would look out at the sea for guidelines. If there was a westerly wind, one expected it to blow its strongest about midday, so in the morning one shouldn't take too much account of the sea at high water if one was planning to go out to get the pots at low water.

Cyril said that he would look at the sea in the outer bay before setting off to whelk, and if the sea were silky and lazy four to five miles off, the wind would be inshore and you could rely on getting the pots in with a fine day for it, with the westerly wind dying at evening time. One wind that could catch the fisherman out was the south-east wind, because inshore there would be hardly any wind, but offshore, if you went six miles off, the further you went out the more wind you would pick up and it could cause you a lot of trouble when trying to pick up the pots in rough weather.

Clear visibility usually meant an easterly wind was to be expected. In early May one could expect these easterly winds, and if it was there before dawn, you knew the wind could come up with the sun, and you could expect a rough day and be tempted not to go out.

In his early fishing career Cyril went out with his uncle. They went out early and about 4.45 a.m. 'the sun would come up lovely like a red blob of light to the north-east', then they knew they were in for a good day, but if it came up 'a red blob and went through a line of loomy weather, like scuddy cloudy weather,' his uncle would remark, 'We're in for a nasty day,' and sure enough the wind would pick up from the east and a swell would come in from the east or south-east.

'I'd go to sea if there was wind then rain,' said Cyril, 'but would stay on shore if rain came before the wind, because that would indicate low pressure was over us.' Cyril said the sky packed with stars was a bad sign and red sky in the morning was sailor's warning; these two signs never failed him in his weather prediction, telling him whether or not he should go to sea or stay ashore.

'Look to the north,' said Cyril, 'and if there are lazy clouds to the north, it is going to fine up, and you can go out as much as two hours after high water, and you'll get your pots, because the wind will die as the tide goes out of the harbour. A north or north-west wind is good for hauling pots and we would come home with a fair wind.'

'A halo round the moon means wet weather, especially October time,' said Cyril. '"Near ring far rain, far ring near rain," is a saying that is rarely wrong. A red moon means a blow, a pale yellow moon means rain and a white moon tells of no rain or snow.'

Candlemas Day (February 2nd) gave the old fishermen an indication of the end of winter and the resumption of the fishing season. So they watched the weather anxiously. An important saying that Cyril found invariably accurate was, 'If Candlemas be fair and bright, winter will have another flight; but if Candlemas be clouds and rain, winter is gone and will not come again.'

'21st March, first day of spring, whichever way the wind is at twelve noon on that day, it will be like that for three months,' was another saying that Cyril took seriously. If it was blowing easterly on that day, they assumed the majority of days to follow would have easterly winds for the three months ahead.

We talked about coastal erosion and flooding. Cyril said that the spring tides in his area are no bigger now than when he was young, and the neap tides no less. His rule of thumb was based on the water level on the mussel lays that he works, and he maintained that the weather in north-west Scotland was largely responsible for our tide height in East Anglia. The '78 surge he remembers well. That morning a force 10 was forecast.

Cyril Southerland at work with his shellfish

'If the tide is on time, the flood warnings can be largely ignored but if the tide is early, that is the important factor in judging whether or not a flood warning is to be taken seriously. A deep low pressure area in January in Scotland should be watched in East Anglia, as that is the critical flood warning indicator for this area. The old fishermen are the best readers of weather, flood warnings and strong wind spells. The shipping forecasts invariably only give a generalised weather picture,' remarked Cyril. In his childhood, he was surrounded by animals and country signs. If his cat went mad, there was wind on the way. If the crows sat high in the tree, that was a sure sign of good weather. Sundogs in the west invariably meant a blow within forty-eight hours.

Cyril discussed one trip he remembered when he got the weather wrong and paid dearly.

'We went out of the harbour one morning about six o'clock and that was when it was raining and it was bad, squally weather. Two or three boats went, one came back, and I thought, "Perhaps it will blow itself out and it's just a squall coming through." As we got going off to the gear, the weather got steadily worse, and the wind had really gripped the sea and it was westerly and so was blowing us towards the gear. Suddenly the waves were surging past us and I was nearly at the gear. I got hold of three of the five shanks so I'd got some weight in the boat. Then I turned for home; that was the only time I saw wisps of the sea boil up. The westerly wind was so intense the waves were hitting the sides of the boat and foam and spray smothered the whole boat. It was a short confused sea and there was so much water everywhere. Normally I would get home from this point in two hours, and it took me three and a half hours because you couldn't drive the boat - I just had to nurse it along. That was one of the worst times I had because I got the weather wrong.'

Men who watch the Weather on Land

Jack, Stephen and Michael Aldred
Thatchers

Stephen Aldred and his brother Michael were trained by their father and love their craft of thatching. 'There is a great demand for good Norfolk reed,' said Stephen. 'I have good memories of each job.'

Stephen was not in an optimistic mood when we talked. 'We may be the last generation of local thatchers. I have two sons, but there is so much more choice of employment these days. Also good Norfolk reed is hard to come by; boys won't go out on the marshes and learn to cut. Soon we'll be importing too much of our reed, but I love my job, although it's hard on the back and the knees, which doesn't get any easier as you get older.'

A thatcher has to work round the weather. 'You can't thatch in the rain,' Stephen explained, 'although ridging could still be done. The art of the thatcher has not changed much over the centuries, and sedge from where old peat diggings were made is cut on a three or four-year cycle between July and October, but is killed off if run over

**Each thatcher is known by his pattern of ridging.
Stephen Aldred at work**

83

by box cutters. A good sedge ridge keeps out wind, snow and rain for up to 30 years and a good thatch may last for 50 years.'

'What do you do in bad weather, stay at home?' I asked.

'We don't miss many days, even in winter, but we can always spend bad weather time to sharpen the hazel brotches.' It was explained to me that brotches (soaked hazel twisted to form a wooden staple) are used to hold the supple sedge in place in the ridge of the building. Each craftsman is known for his pattern of ridging.

Stephen told me that thatchers need to plan their thatching work for a spell of good weather. The signs he notes are red sky at night, birds singing a full dawn chorus and a clear sky in the distance beyond overhead rain. He pointed out that easterly winds were cold ones, but the weather could be bright with clear skies, whilst southerly winds in summer gave the thatcher an expectation of a good day's thatching, as also would clear skies overnight with a riming frost the night before.

Signs of wind, not so pleasant for the thatcher, were listed: seagulls moving inland, a higher cloud base, a calm before the storm and a stillness prior to the wind arriving.

Weather conditions that hampered the thatcher's art were listed: low clouds and south-westerly winds, a build-up of high humidity in the summer, a change in the temperature and a cloud front approaching in the distance. 'Sometimes you can smell the rain approaching in the air around you,' commented Stephen.

Both brothers and their father watched the clouds, and said that stratocumulus and nimbostratus clouds brought them rain and murky weather whilst cirrus clouds brought in storms. Fluffy white cumulus clouds were a promise of good weather and good thatching conditions.

The best weather for cutting reeds was a long period of easterly winds. In winter, cold easterly winds came in from Siberia, and sharp frosts, blizzards and snow settling could be expected. Also the water levels would go down, ideal for reed-cutting. At present Stephen and Michael have a three-month job on a large house in Norfolk.

Jack Aldred, father to Stephen and Michael, left school at fourteen and went to work on the local farm. He was born in 1928 at Martham. When his father was away on war service, Jack lived with his grandfather, who was a reed-cutter and thatcher. They lived in a thatched cottage. The grandfather said to his grandson one day, 'Go out on that old rond.' He wanted to know whether the selected patch

84

of meadow was good to put the grazing cattle on. The boy walked out on to the marsh and stood still; his hand grasped something hard so he looked down and found that he had taken hold of the upturned beak of a bittern. She had not deserted her nest as the boy strode up to her and he almost walked over her nest.

Jack, cutting reed in the 1940s, recalled that on a foggy February day foghorns could be heard wailing out seaward, and bitterns on the marshes at Ling's, where he was working, were answering back.

Jack at work on a Norfolk house

Cocks crowing continuously during the day indicated rain on the way. Hens took shelter if a shower of rain was expected, but they would stay outside if more continuous rain were on its way. Cows lying down in the fields also suggested rain was expected. Curlews called and swallows flew low before rain. Gulls flying in circles indicated that rain and wind was approaching. Owls flying during daylight hours meant wind could be expected. Pigs running about with straw in their mouths was a certain sign that wind and rain was on its way. If chimney smoke went straight upwards a fine day could be assured, but if the smoke swirled downwards from the chimney tops, wind and rain was a certainty. If the rain and wind came in from

85

the east, it would last for twenty-four hours at least. A 'sun dog' in the sky indicated a deterioration in the weather, and a 'water cart' in the sky meant rain.

If the cattle were unsettled, wind could be expected, and if the weather was very still, one should be aware that it was the calm before the storm.

Such close observation of animals and skies could only be expected from a country craftsman such as Jack. As a boy farm worker, and later as an eminent thatcher in Norfolk, he had the opportunity to watch nature all around him while he worked.

One of my favourite views in the world is walking down a path beside Hickling Broad. A cluster of old boat houses line the east shore of the Broad. Inside are stored some fabulous historic Broadland wooden yachts. Jack thatched one of these sheds recently and daily I walked past, watching a seventy-something-year-old man creating a glorious thatched roof. His work will long outlast the whole family.

Beside Hickling Broad

86

Kenny Beales
Farm worker and Gardener

Kenny Beales was born in Hickling in 1928. He attended the local village school until he reached the age of fourteen. His first job was at Stubb Farm as a land worker. From 1951-72 Kenny worked at the Pleasure Boat Inn. The public house gardens and a smallholding supplied Mr and Mrs Gwen Amis, the public house owners, with fresh vegetables and fruit. Pigs, chickens and bullocks were also reared to supply fresh meat. Most men growing up in Hickling went to sea, fishing for a living. The alternative was to work on the land, and Kenny worked on four farms before transferring to a job with Anglian Water.

Remembering his own childhood, Kenny remarked that he was sorry for modern children; his own grandchildren could no longer cycle to schools in surrounding towns like Stalham. 'They are out of contact with nature more than we were,' he said sadly.

Kenny's father and his brothers were fishermen, working on trawlers and drifters out of Yarmouth, and as a child he recalled playing on the beach, and being told always to face the sea - never turn his back on the sea and to be aware that every fourth wave was the biggest of the cycle. Coming from a fishing family, Kenny learnt that there were fish about if the seagulls collected, and to watch the moon and tides because good weather could be expected if they ran together. As Kenny grew up, he learnt to use ferrets to catch rabbits; he also learnt to trap moles and shoot vermin. As I walked to Kenny's peaceful cottage, just outside Hickling village, he was returning from a farm, where the farmer had requested him to shoot the pigeon pests; on the way past his allotment, he had picked a bag of fresh vegetables for his wife. He greeted me with a true countryman's comment, 'Did you see the rainbow last evening? It went right down into the sea, so I knew we were in for some rough weather.' Hours later, after I had absorbed fascinating stories, Kenny put his bicycle away; glancing up at the sky, he said, 'Rain coming in, the water butts are full,' and he pointed out a line of black nimbus clouds bubbling up over the garden from the west.

I asked Kenny to tell me about bad weather signs he had watched over the past sixty or so years. His list:- 'If you see a green or bronze light in the sky, bad weather's on its way; if birds go quiet, wind is on its way, rooks will stop feeding and go home by midday (normally they are first out and last home); seagulls will come inland by early afternoon if there are no lug worms to be dug up by the bait-diggers; if pigs run about with straw in their mouths, and their tails straight out, if cats, dogs and horses get excited and run about irrationally, or if pigeons roost low or birds feed frantically - these are all signs that wind and rain are approaching. Wild birds feed up to within half an hour of sunset normally, but if they feel a storm approaching will come in to feed early, as much as two to three hours earlier; if there is a bad smell over the flight ponds - these are all indications of the approach of wind and rain.'

Regarding the behaviour of birds, Kenny had observed that if the geese arrive early and are heading north, bad weather is coming in from the south and vice-versa. Chickens and hens will take cover before a showery spell but will stay outside and feed if a longer spell of rain is predicted. Most birds won't fly in wind and rain, but will fly before wind arrives, using it to their advantage. 'If cockerels crow a lot, rain's on its way,' I was told.

On the subject of hot weather, Kenny said birds will avoid flying and chickens will hide away; a heavy early morning dew on the grass suggests a hot day ahead, but an over-bright morning 'is too bright to last' and if there is no dew, there'll be a shower before sunset. When there is a full moon, birds will go very quiet. 'You can hear a twig

88

break,' said Kenny, 'but in moonlight, owls will shriek.' The full moon affects many creatures including humans. 'I let the dogs out to catch rabbits at full moon. They are more excited and lively,' he said.

'People get caught by frosts,' remarked Kenny. 'If the sun is setting when the moon is rising, we'll get a dawn frost.'

On the subject of wind, Kenny said that 'an easterly wind will drain us dry, and a westerly wind will fill us up'. He was talking about the Broad draining in drying easterly wind and filling with rain-bearing westerly winds. One evening he walked up to the allotments at night and discovered a hoard of rats eating the turnips. 'Dog got forty rats,' he commented. Four days later, 'Broad was up, swollen by severe rain.' On another occasion, a hoard of rats came up from Catfield, to gorge on acorns. Three days later the north-west wind brought flooding and the level of the Broad rose noticeably. On an earlier occasion, in the 1940s Kenny found 300 rats in one bale of straw, and in one shed more than 100 rats were cornered. Two days later, westerly winds brought flooding to that area.

Talking about his vegetable-growing, Kenny remarked that he liked to grow his runner beans on the ground, pointing out that pollinating insects worked best out of the wind. He said butterflies and moths seek for nectar in low-growing plants and prefer not to fly higher than necessary, where wind may block their progress, or birds eat them. He had seen jays eating butterflies, and sparrows got moths that ventured too high in the vegetation. He also remarked that the higher the swarms of flying insects, the warmer would be the day, as they were evidence of the rising thermals.

Two days before I met Kenny, I had gone out from Hickling Sailing Club, intent on enjoying the peace and tranquillity of the Broad at dawn. As so many times before, I sailed down to Martham in a wonderful, watery world, beneath an endless blue sky, gold reeds bending in the breeze and a miracle of insect sounds in the reed beds and marshy edges of the river.

Three hours later I ate breakfast aboard *Wanderbug*, then turned back for the sailing club. As I beat along, the light headwinds made progress pleasant. On the last bend in the river before entering the Broad, all hell was suddenly let loose on the water, while spume flicked across my face, and looking across the Broad I stared in disbelief at walls of water and white-flecked waves roaring across Hickling Broad. Not really believing what I had witnessed, I began to beat across the broad, and twice was nearly overpowered. I rushed into a reed bed and furled the jib and reefed the mainsail, then carried on beating. Water roared over my whole body and the water in my small 11-foot dinghy reached up to the thwarts.

An hour later, my friend, who was due to meet me for a day's sail, stood on the club pontoons on a bright sunny calm morning looking in disbelief at my sodden boat and shivering body, before helping me dry out my dinghy. 'Oh, you've sailed through a "Jolly Roger",' said Sid Wren, our club caretaker and a Broads boatman of some seventy years.

Later Kenny explained what a 'Roger' was. It is a local name for a sudden violent summer storm, caused as rising warm air gets trapped between layers of cooler air. 'I once saw a waterspout over the Broad,' said Kenny. 'A storm will not go over water, so it escaped over towards Yarmouth, but a waterspout drew up frogs and small fish out of the Broad and then dropped them back over the Broad...I have seen straw bales picked up in the air and scattered over the fields in another violent whirlwind, and I've known roofs taken off and dust spiralling upwards over fields as a summer Jolly Roger hits us.'

Finally Kenny told me about a long-gone Norfolk occupation. 'I used to go eel-babbing if a storm was brewing. In 1953 I caught a 4½lb eel. Eels run best before a storm. Give me a black night and rain, then they'll run. Fish will feed best before or after rain. At one time you could pull all kind of fish out of the Broad. The insects on the waterweed gave them so much to feed on. Now the Broad is opaque and nearly lifeless.'

Some months had gone by, and I chanced to walk past the village allotments. It did not surprise me to find Kenny's large allotment was beautifully kept and very productive. 'I've had an allotment for 50 years. I took one the year I married, in 1951. In the early days I grew a lot of fruit, except strawberries - it was too wet for them. Nowadays I grow vegetables.' He explained how he planted all his seeds at the growing moon phase - then they kept going. Other tips I learnt were to get the pollinating bees early in the season - then they would stay all year. Instead of planting one type of vegetable, for example broad beans, Kenny would mix his bean seed varieties, to ensure a long season's crop, as the broad beans would mature at different times, thus ensuring continuous cropping and a continuous set of visits from the pollinators, like bees. 'It's the same with my hens,' he explained. 'I stagger my animals' ages and breeding stock, so the taste, supply and health of my chickens remains excellent. Farmers nowadays haven't the time or the profit margins to do more than just rush out the crop, bury in more fertilizer and plant the next crop. There's no flavour in modern crops.'

Kenny Beales working his allotment

Our conversation turned to weather. 'People used to look for the weather years ago; if the sun comes up that bright you can't look at it, good weather won't last the day, and if it goes down too bright so you can't look at it, the weather is going to be poor for a day or two. I'd rather see a red sun going down and coming up because you know you're going to have settled weather for gardening for a day or two. If you see the rabbits out feeding in the afternoon - also the rats - you can be sure it's going to be a wet evening. They don't like to eat wet food. Birds too, they'll keep well fed before a storm approaches. If you look out and see a starry night, bad weather is on its way and you won't want to dig the ground for a day or two.

Everything is changing today,' said Kenny. 'In my youth you could depend on the seasons, and growing foods was predictable. These days we seem to get such violent changes, like huge winds and heavy rainstorms and indifferent temperatures, nothing very cold, or

91

predictable, no long hot spells in the summer months, or deep frosts and snowdrifts that kept the pests under control. In my youth the marshes would flood up and one night's frost would freeze over the slades, and we could skate on them. The old windmills had a gentle action and the water would swirl around the marshes gently. Nowadays, the rivers are dredged deeper, the pumps are more powerful, and the water gushes everywhere. In the old days my brother Arthur, a marshman, would scythe one side of the dyke at a time; the other side was left for wild things to shelter in and for wild plants to seed themselves. In times gone by, scything was done by hand; now machinery cuts all the vegetation down low. People years ago tended their land by hand and the flood water would escape. In modern times there is so much building and concrete landscaping, the water has nowhere to escape to, and flooding is becoming a problem.'

'If the moon comes up nice and hard you know you're going to get a fine spell and can get on with the digging. That sign works now as it did years ago. Again, when you get a change in the wind direction, you get a change in the weather and if the tides don't run with the moon, bad weather will be expected. But nowadays things are less predictable: one half of the village may get rain whilst the other half stays dry. The old saying, that if you got your feet wet when you went out first thing in the morning it would be a fine day, can no longer be relied on, and we used to think if there was no morning dew, it would rain by sunset - but in these times the weather is most unpredictable.'

Kenny told me about severe electrical storms years ago. He recalled that in his mother's time, in the 1930s, in the month of June, he and a farm worker were out working with a horse when a violent thunder and lightning storm roared in. The two men went to shelter in a nearby barn. 'I threw a sack over the horse to keep him warm and dry,' said Kenny. 'Suddenly, a thunderbolt hit my partner, hurled him across the barn. An ancient oak tree nearby lost all its leaves. They turned brown overnight then dropped off.'

In my own childhood in the '40s I remember violent summer storms, but in recent years there seems to have been less extreme summer heat. However, in June 2001 I witnessed close at hand a very violent thunderstorm over Hickling Broad. In East Anglia we had enjoyed a glorious heat wave, with temperatures hovering between 70 and 80°F. for a whole week. 'Thunderstorms will cross the region from the west,' said the evening local weather forecast. Being woken after midnight by thunder and lightning and violent rain showers, I assumed the storms had gone out to sea. Up at 05.00 hours the following day, I prepared to sail from Hickling to Horsey, and rigged my eleven-foot dinghy and launched on a quiet dawn. Within a short time, distant thunderclaps roared in, and seemed to tear about over my head very low in ever-decreasing circles with huge flashes of lightning darting all over the water. Having Wellington boots in my camping gear, I hove-to and put them on, then carried on sailing until I realized this was no ordinary storm. Considering sailing into the river to shelter from the waves that were building on the Broad, with white frothing foam scudding over angry grey turbulent water, I realized the rivers had too many trees lining them, so decided to sail back to skulk beneath the moored yachts that had higher masts than my 21-foot metal mast. Suddenly a violent force hit my shoulder accompanied by the loudest clap of thunder I have ever heard. Thrown forward in my dinghy I looked up to see if I had capsized, and saw blue light flashing down my shrouds. When the rain came, minutes later, it was of monsoon intensity.

Later when I related this storm experience to Kenny, he said, 'You earthed the thunderbolt. Had you not been wearing rubber boots, things might have ended differently.' He then said that storms usually intensify over the Broad, then escape out to sea along the rivers. This time the cloud cover was so low that the electricity could not escape, so roared back and forth across the Broad in an attempt to get away.

The ferocity of that storm put the computerised weather-line system at Hickling Sailing Club out of action. All electrical appliances in the surrounding village homes were also put out of action.

I was glad to have witnessed such a memorable storm. Quite unforgettable.

Frank Dye

Businessman, agricultural engineer and long-distance dinghy sailor

Frank, a businessman and agricultural engineer, was born in Watton, Norfolk, in 1928 and learnt to sail on the Norfolk Broads. He picked up his weather knowledge almost unconsciously when working as a tractor mechanic in the open sandy Breckland of south Norfolk, and also from the farm labourers on the more populated small farms of central Norfolk when eating his lunch sandwiches with them.

'It was essential to get the weather right; bad weather coming in meant finding cover for the machinery before stripping down - probably a cart shed - and this might involve moving out heavy farm waggons single-handed. If it didn't rain farmers sometimes objected to such wasted time; and the penalty of misjudging the weather was a soaking and a telling-off for "letting rainwater get inside the cogs." The 50s and 60s was a fascinating time for the young mechanic with diesel engines replacing TVO (tractor vaporising oil), and hydraulics displacing drag implements. It taught flexibility and improvisation. The description of the fault 'phoned in by the farmer's wife wasn't always accurate, and every repair job was different. For example, the standard method of "making" a hydraulic joint was a mixture of "tow" (teased out rope) and red haematite sealer, but sometimes you forgot, or another mechanic had borrowed from your toolbox, and then you had to catch one of the farm horses and pull half-a-dozen hairs from its tail, which coated with sealer did the job just as well.'

Fog and thunderstorms were included in the learning curve, but they are weather phenomena that Frank has never been happy with. He told me that in the 40s and 50s fog was much worse than now. It was dense, yellow, acrid and choking, heavily polluted by domestic fires and industrial smoke from the cities. It was appropriately named 'smog'. One year all the animals at the Smithfield Fat Stock Show in London were fitted with masks over their nostrils to keep them alive. Driving near the cities was only possible by following a flashlight held by a passenger feeling his way along the roadside. Frank recollected as a boy walking along the kerb showing a torch to his father driving behind, losing the kerbstones and leading a queue of cars and vans round the deserted Norwich speedway track. After dirty, open household coal fires were banned in the 60s, fog became cleaner and less persistent.

It is generally believed that sound in fog is unreliable, but this is not completely true. Frank has found that fog seems to skip from one fog bank to the next so that there are dead places where you cannot hear a loud noise almost next door, whilst far sounds are clear. Sound direction, on the other hand, can be relied on. Fog is difficult to predict without instruments and it creeps in unnoticed in little wisps. It is disorientating, especially at sea; sometimes magnifying, or shrinking, distant objects, and always distorting so that a plant on the mud becomes a tree, or a gannet on a rock drying its wings, glimpsed through a gap in fog, is a building on a far headland, or a swirl in a fog bank is the outline of a great cliff overhanging the mast head. Only the compass can be trusted.

Frank didn't start sailing until he was 27 years old. Attempting to teach himself the rudiments of boat-handling, he took his first aluminium dinghy and launched at Wroxham Broad on a Sunday morning. Unable to control the course of his dinghy against the head wind, he heard an irate Officer-of-the-Day bellow out over the loud-speaker system, 'Get that bloody tin boat off my start line.'

Frank says that he received another lesson when he started sailing along the coast. One weekend he sailed at Blakeney with his new Wayfarer dinghy. 'That's one of the new Wayfarers, isn't it?' said Ted Eales, the warden of Blakeney Point nature reserve. 'What are you going to do with it?' Without thinking Frank replied, 'I thought I'd sail to Scotland for a start.' Ted, a typical Norfolk man, assumed he was dealing with another 'know-it-all' and proceeded to 'take him down a peg', and Frank remarked wryly, 'He stuck more lies and exaggeration into me in the next half-hour than I have ever believed before or since.' It was a well-deserved lesson. There is a vast reservoir of knowledge of local weather and the resultant sea conditions amongst the fishermen, bait-diggers, wardens and those who work the salt marshes, which they are willing to share, but tact is needed. From such people Frank learned to weigh up the weather probabilities and developed his ability to snatch passages during short weather windows.

Modern yachtsmen get regular forecasts as they travel the world in their boats. The wonders of satellite navigation and sophisticated communication give them an up-to-date picture of the depressions and cyclones in their vicinity. Frank carried only a small radio receiver and radio direction-finder set in the open cockpit of his dinghy.

Generally, when he set out, after studying weather records going back several years, and preparing the boat, he and his crew realized they relied mostly on their own judgement of sea conditions and ability to read the weather. Listening to the locals, fishermen or landsmen also gave great insight into local weather patterns and sea conditions.

In Frank's most recent book, *Sailing to the Edge of Fear*, he describes sailing his 16ft boat single-handed along the American and Canadian coast and into the Great Lakes. Some extracts from his log books reveal the pleasures and pains of small boat cruising in such vast waters and explain that weather conditions can make all the difference between life and death. His logs note:

'Thunderstorms are different. Fortunately in our temperate U.K. climate thunderstorms are rare, at worst accompanied by heavy rain and strong winds. But in hotter countries their violence is unbelievable, but the locals learn to live with them.'

'The Great Lakes are enormous inland seas, situated in the hot plains of the mid-West, and the local thunderstorms are unbelievably violent, developing quickly and giving little warning apart from Thunderstorm Watch warnings on the wireless, and often accompanied by hailstones, sometimes the size of cricket balls. I had become complacent and nearly paid the price. An illustration of how the weather is always the master follows below.

13th July 1995. Green Bay Wisconsin USA. Escanaba to Gladstone. This six-mile passage was nearly my last! With the benefit of hindsight I was becoming complacent.

The radio forecast of 94°F with excessive humidity and a Heat Advisory Warning was going to make the day uncomfortable. In light southerly winds I cast off for Gladstone. Several people shouted across had I heard the warnings of morning thunderstorms, some very violent? But there was no sign of any thunderclouds building, and I decided 'Green Bay is a big area 100 miles long so it's long odds any storm will miss me, and I don't mind getting wet.' By noon the radio Thunderstorm Watch had expired and I began to relax. A greyness appeared low on the horizon to the north-west, but with little height to it, there were no thunderheads, the wind remained light from the north, and I thought, 'Ah, a light rain shower'. So I pulled on my oilskins. With sudden shock I realised that the greyness was approaching at enormous speed and I scrambled down two reefs and furled the genoa. With incredible power the wind hit. The ferocity almost lifted *Wanderer* out of the water as it got under the bilge as the hull rose to the crest of a wave. White water was blown instantly to smoke, *Wanderer* rolled her lee gun'l under, and water poured aboard. I jumped forward, and got the deep-reefed sail down, fortunately nothing snarled up or fouled, but I wasn't safe yet. *Wanderer* was broadside, the wind the most furious I have experienced. My only hope was to get her running downwind under bare poles before the wind under her bilge lifted her bodily out of the water as she rose to each crest, and only the weight of water in the bilges prevented a capsize. It was a hectic few minutes - no time to think - reacting instinctively! The Escanaba yacht harbour had disappeared into the murk, but I took a quick compass bearing on the powerful flash of the lighthouse before it disappeared, but with the way the seas were building, I knew that I could not survive to reach that shelter. Instead, with quartering seas and centreboard down, I decided to run under bare mast behind the long ore dock, hoping to get a line ashore before being blown away to leeward. Torrential rain hammered the seas down, everything disappeared except the vague shadow of the shipping terminal a few yards away. I got ready to throw a line to two shadowy men waving on the end of the dock, but as I got nearer they became two bushes waving in the storm. I luffed, was blown away, grabbed the oars and rowed desperately until close enough to grab hold and pass a line round a pile. Lightning was sizzling overhead, instantaneous thunder ear-deafening above, storm-driven rain reducing visibility to almost nothing.

For an hour I cowered behind the dock, wet through, and waiting for the storm to blow out. By 2 p.m., the wind had slackened and veered, and I almost went overboard casting off, as my lifeline jammed in the dock face, with *Wanderer* rising and falling even behind the dock. The boat was a shambles, gear blown overboard and everything covered with a thick layer of brown ore dust as I sailed for Gladstone; the thunderstorm had passed away eastwards behind me. Several days later I met the crew of a yacht downwind of me by a few miles during the storm. Their wind indicator had jammed - at 60 knots! 'How did you manage?' they asked me. 'Did you motor into it?' They couldn't believe that anyone would cruise without a motor.

Eric Edwards
Reed-cutter

Eric Edwards retains the skill of a nearly lost art, that of cutting Norfolk reeds by hand. Most reeds are cut by machine these days, but to see Eric preparing his scythe, it is plain to see that he enjoys his working life to the full.

Eric was born in Ling Eastern and his first job after completing school was to work at Walnut Tree Farm. In 1967 he was employed by the Broads Authority to manage How Hill reed beds and grazing marshes. 'Today the reeds are looking good,' Eric enthused. 'Things are coming back. I see the bearded tit and bittern around, and water lilies are back in the dykes.' Eric admits to using machinery to cut the reed as well as his scythes, but says with honesty, 'People used to work the marshes years ago, and the old ways are best. The old marshmen were clever; they had an eye for materials and could use tools caringly.'

Eric told me how he worked. 'Mowing is hard graft. I reckon it'll all be gone soon. The young don't want to learn this kind of work.' He explained how the reed is cut on the marshes, done in a double whale once every two years, opposite sides of the dyke taken alternate years, to leave vegetation for wildlife like the bearded tit and swallowtail butterfly. 'Reed is cut between Christmas and April when the leaf is off before the new colt emerge.'

The earliest reed-cutters, the fishermen, used a fathom as a standard measurement; five to six bunches making up one fathom. Then they were thumped down on a drouncing board, dressed and tied in bundles. 'Never tie up the reeds when they are wet,' said Eric, 'or they'll never dry out. I've cut in water a lot this year (2000 was the wettest year ever), there has been a lot of rain. Before I plan my day I look at the old mill - if it's westerly, the water will pour up. The old reed-cutters used to say that it would rain soon if the feathers on top of the reed closed up.'

'I look forward to Mondays and going back on the marshes; how many men can say that?' said Eric, his ruddy face beaming. 'When the reed is dry and the feather loose on the winter stem, it glistens gold, and is a beautiful sight.'

Reed Lighter with Eric Edwards at the stern

We haven't had many easterly winds yet this spring, but when they arrive and we get a cold spell, the water table will go down and I'll have a good day on the marshes, because the east winds take the water away just as the west winds bring the water up. A reed-cutter has to work round the weather. They used to say the old fishermen who cut the reeds were lazy and always drinking, but they were wise enough to know you couldn't cut the reeds until they were dried out, so they sat in the pubs until the reeds became ready to work on.'

Mardling with Eric made me recall that the Broads are man-made. The flooded peat-diggings started in Roman times reaching peak production over the period from 12th century-14th century. In the late 13th century rising sea levels and climatic changes caused the 'turve' collection, blocks of peat, to come to an end. By the 15th century peat-digging was virtually a thing of the past and the flooded straight-sided Broads formed and became the commercial watery roadways through Broadland. Open water was quickly colonised by reeds *(Phragmites cummums)* and sedge *(Cladium mariscus)* also became established.

Norfolk reed, considered to be some of the best in Europe, is today an excellent commercial harvest, and houses are thatched with reed all over England, while the more pliable sedge is utilised on the

99

house ridges. Eric Edwards transports his reed, cut in the winter, and sedge, cut in the summer, by a reed lighter which he quants along the rivers. Vikings used similar clinker-built longboats, and the ones used today are direct descendants of these Viking boats.

Many of the locals living round Hickling say that the Broad generates its own weather. George and Johnny are my Sunday sailing friends. Their experience in sailing dinghies on the Broads goes back more than fifty years. I learn from them every time we push their ancient Wayfarer out from Hickling dyke. They never listen to the forecasts as they drive down to the Broad from Norwich and Ludham. 'We'll go down and take a look,' they always say, and our winter sails, past the reed beds with the sun glinting on them fringing the river ways, are something quite special.

Patrick J. A. Gowen J.P. MIST
Head of the North Sea Action Group

Pat Gowen was born in Norwich in 1932, attending Crooke's Place, later known as Bignold School, and going on to Thorpe Hamlet, both of which he was bombed out of. Pat then went to Cromer School, leaving at fourteen to work at the Public Analyst's at fifteen shillings per sixty-hour week. Nevertheless, he saved enough to enable him to attend the local Technical College and Art School for a year, supplementing his meagre income by working at the Post Office over Christmas and the Miller Organ Company during the summer break.

His working experience has included working on public analysis, retail, commercial and hospital pharmacy, radiography, electronic research and design and food research. Finally, Pat joined the Biophysical Department in the School of Biological Sciences at the University of East Anglia as a founder member. The administrative side involved more and more paper work, and for contrast Pat used to go out with the local fishermen. He learnt to see how these local weather-wise fishermen always operated with an eye out to sea. 'Boy, we'd better start getting the nets up, there's a blow coming in,' one might say as the cumulus clouds bubbled up over the horizon. Pat watched another navigating by lining up the shoreline sights and by back-bearing use of his compass.

There was an opportunity for early retirement in his early fifties, and Pat retired in 1983. He then launched into a self-made career. He started the North Sea Action Group, for he regarded the threat to the North Sea as work for us all. Over-fishing, damaging our seas with over-dredging, and infecting our seas with sewage systems are subjects he feels passionate about. Everything is changing rapidly, and Pat feels that the weather is also changing, Southern Europe possibly becoming a desert within our lifetime, water shortages and little winter snow a strong possibility, and many weather patterns becoming more intensified around the world.

Whilst many of the people I have talked to are concerned with weather watch, Pat is the exception, in that his passion is in *water* watch. In March 1988 he and his wife lost their coastal bungalow as a direct result of coastal erosion, which he felt was accelerated by

Pat Gowen's bungalow, 'Riskit', falling from the cliffs at Winterton

offshore aggregate dredging. He is aware that global warming may be partly responsible for the rise in sea levels, with serious threat to East Anglian coastal areas, and that ever-increasing emissions from power stations, industry and traffic have resulted in rising sea levels and the Greenhouse Effect. There is therefore a serious need to take action before planet Earth not only loses its benign weather patterns, which we have been able to rely on and predict for thousands of years, but also loses the very soil and beaches of the coastal area where we now live.

Pat Gowen produced the *Good Beach Guide* in 1996. Each beach situated in Norfolk, Suffolk, Lincolnshire and Essex was tested for its water quality, with other coastal resort information included. A section on coastal erosion, called 'Our disappearing coastline' makes chilling reading. The book is charmingly illustrated by Norma Gowen, Pat's wife, an accomplished artist.

Pat Gowen continues his interest in communications, writing articles in many international radio magazines. He has researched and written reports for the European Environmental Bureau, and has given evidence and produced papers to the 1989-90 House of Commons Environmental Committee into the Pollution of Beaches and to the 1997-98 Department of the Environment, Trade and the Regions Affairs Committee Enquiry into Sewage Treatment and Disposal. He has also provided evidence to DG-X1 of the European Commission resulting in the prosecutions of Britain over the failure to meet European directives. It was these interests and concerns on public health issues, combined with radio communications research and practical experience in the field of VHF and UHF, that led to his investigation into the potential biological hazards of exposure to very high and ultra-high-frequency radio fields.

Pat Gowen was a founder member of the Norwich City Council's Hazards Committee and the Broadland Environmental Forum for both of which he produced papers on various environmental and health concerns. He was a founder member of AMSAT, an organisation in which he served as a director for six years, also working on the practical design and operation of equipment and the propagational aspects of antennae for VHF and UHF satellites and their base stations.

Two of Pat Gowen's many papers are reproduced in this book by kind permission of the author. (See Appendix 1 & 2)

Ray Loose
Gardener

Ray Loose was born in Snettisham in 1920. I listened in as he celebrated his 80th birthday on air a few days ago on the gardening programme broadcast on Radio Norfolk.

Ray's grandfather had several acres of Norfolk marshes at Snettisham. On them he looked after the farmer's stock of horses, cows and sheep. 'They were all dykes and no hedges in those days,' said Ray, 'and the sheep often had to be hauled out of the dykes.' As a child, Ray had a pony, and at weekends he rode around his grandfather's marshes. Ray's father was a keen gardener, and when Ray came out of the Navy at the end of the war, having travelled widely and been employed as a gunnery instructor, his need for peacetime employment drew him back to the land. He became head gardener working for the Gurney family who lived at Keswick Hall, Norfolk. 'I went all over England, and we did very well with our sweet pea shows,' said Ray. 'From the Keswick Hall gardens there was a huge demand for fresh vegetables and fruit, especially when there were shooting parties and house party weekends.'

Talking to Ray just before he was due to go out live on air, I asked if he would like to be left to wait quietly. 'Aren't you nervous?' I said. 'You never know what kind of gardening subjects are coming up.'

'After over twenty years talking about gardening problems on radio, I'm not nervous,' said Ray. 'I just enjoy listening to people's queries.' In 1978 Ray took part in a radio programme called 'Round about East Anglia'. When Radio Norfolk was established about 20 years ago he joined them and has been talking gardening twice weekly ever since.

His hobby is fly-fishing. Sometimes Mr Richard Gurney would ring home saying, 'Get everything ready. We'll go trout fishing.' So Ray's hobby sprang from those fishing trips from Keswick Hall. Ray makes his own flies for fishing; his wife says he used to teach fly-fishing and is even more addicted to fishing than gardening and loves 'to read the water'.

In 1986 Mr and Mrs Ray Loose left Keswick Hall and moved to Thatched Cottage at Bawdeswell.

'Keswick Hall was a special place in the 1930-50s,' recalled Ray. 'Everybody helped one another; the sense of village community was

very strong. If two cattle were killed, everybody got something. The villagers lived by barter; money was rarely exchanged.'

At Thatched Cottage Mr and Mrs Loose rapidly established a garden, and it has been opened to the public for the past twenty years, proceeds going to the Red Cross.

Listening to Ray in the live broadcast was a great experience; he was completely natural and relaxed, and his wealth of experience enabled him to identify with each caller's gardening problems. It is obvious that a good and successful gardener has to be aware of weather both in the short and long term. One lady called in complaining that the winter-flowering pansies looked sick. 'There's been 9 inches extra rainfall in Norfolk this year,' commented Ray. 'Your pansies just need some sun and warmth.'

Another caller asked about his poor tomato crop in the previous summer. 'It was a very wet summer, cold nights, little sun and low light levels - great weather for rot, and the worst tomato-growing season I can ever remember,' said Ray. Rainfall and water supplies to the garden dominated each conversation as another Norfolk listener asked how he should avoid potato blight for a second successive year.

Ray's father told him, 'If you can't eat it, don't grow it.' Ray said, 'A kitchen garden is a lifestyle,' and he went on to explain that you can't fight nature. He pointed out that weather is changing, but whether this is due to cyclic patterns or the Greenhouse Effect is open to debate. 'When we first moved to Bawdeswell, thick icicles would freeze solid and hang down from the thatch to the ground, and not melt for weeks. Now it is often colder at Easter than it is at Christmas.' Being aware of the changing weather trends is essential for a successful gardener, and Ray pointed out that with the summers growing dryer, and rainfall patterns changing, it was stupid to continue to grow celery, a thirsty crop, so instead he grew celeriac, which did not require so much water.

Ray also remembered past winters when there were deep frosts, and the frogspawn would hatch, but the frogs couldn't return to the streams because they were frozen; herons would be seen feeding on the fields where the frogs were trapped, and the streamlets frozen so they could not be used either by frogs or herons.

On the subject of planting-out times, Ray advised against planting out tender plants unless the weather was right. When there is a full moon and clear skies, you can get hard frosts as late as May and even early June, not the time to transplant tender cuttings. Another lady was advised to 'root her cuttings around the edge of the pot, where they would dry out less rapidly.'

Ray talked about his close family. 'We all got together round the table to talk about the weather when you asked me to remember some old folk lore,' he explained.

Most of the weather predictions Ray listed I had not met before. 'If you find a frog that looks yellow, the weather will be fine; if it is going to be wet within a few hours, the same frog will turn dark brown or green.'

'If a pale brimstone butterfly appears early in the season after a spell of bad weather, then a spell of fine weather may be expected.'

'If a cockerel crows long before dawn it predicts rain, or if it is winter, snow is on the way.'

Ray also said that if there were lots of holly berries it foretold a hard winter. (Other people have told me, however, that a good harvest of holly berries denoted a mild spring, when good pollination was in evidence).

Ray made a comment that seemed to typify a contented countryman. 'I haven't made a lot of money, but I've had a rich life.'

Arthur Stockdale
Estate worker

Visiting Arthur in his remote Norfolk house was refreshing in that the family lived in a cosy home surrounded by open fields. The teenage children delighted in their animals; rare breeds of chicken and bantams ran free in the lawned front garden, where beautifully-made wooden huts were their open homes. Two pigmy goats were housed to the side of the house in roomy sheds. Arthur's finely-restored tractors, four of them, dating from 1931 to 1950, occupied a large part of the garden and shared the outhouses with a hut of guinea pigs. A friendly cat and pug dog greeted me. 'We are not bothered by neighbours,' was Arthur's comment as he got out his large collection of family albums of photographs and press cuttings. Arthur was born in 1927 in Suffolk on the Henham Estate owned by the Earl of Stradbrooke, and run by a huge army of employees. The estate was run rather on the feudal style, and the six villages comprising the estate ran seventeen farms on which could be found brick and cement works, corn mills, wheelwrights, blacksmiths and every necessary business to make the estate totally self-sufficient.

Arthur was educated at the local village school then went straight into work with his father on the farm, where his grandfather, uncle, aunts and cousins were all employed. Arthur's father was farm manager, and Arthur recalls working with Suffolk Punches, St Kilda sheep and long-horned Scots cows. Crossing Scots cows with Aberdeen Angus resulted in an uncontrollable herd. 'They were mad,' Arthur remembered. 'We couldn't unload them, we had to shoot them in the field.'

In Arthur's painstakingly compiled photographic record of his family working on the Henham Estate, I enjoyed photographs of his uncle and father working with the horses. There was a handwritten letter from the Earl of Stradbrooke to his grandfather, and a photograph of the last field of barley being scythed.

The parkland on which the herds grazed was ploughed up as part of the Second World War effort. Instead of meadows, wheat, corn and barley were sown in rotation. Only in the 1980s did the land get put back to grass.

Arthur's father and uncle on the farm

From October to January, when the herring season was over, many fishermen migrated to the farms to work on the land during the winter. 'They were good old boys,' recalled Arthur. 'They were responsible for my interest in the weather. Even today, I think about what they told me - and they were never far out with their predictions.' Whilst working on the farm, the fishermen would clean out the ditches around the marshes, work in the woods, cutting out the old trees, and keep the miles of hedging in good shape. 'There was no weather forecasting in those days,' explained Arthur, 'so we listened careful to what they told us.'

'If you see wisps of clouds high up in the sky, it will be windy. The old fisher boys called them "mares' tails", and if you look up at the sky on a cloudy day and the clouds can get away - they are not all hemmed in - then you can be sure it will not rain. If there are patches of cloud and you can pick out a small wisp of cloud and it gets bigger, then you can expect rain, but if that small wisp melts away it should be fine all day.'

The fishermen also told the farm boys to look at the sun on a dull day; if there was a 'sun dog' on the sides of the sun, it would surely bring wet weather.

'We were early risers on the farm,' remarked Arthur, 'and the fishermen told us to look at the dawn sky. If the sun in the morning comes up in a red sky and the red goes right over, it will be fine, but if it comes up and then falls back, it will be a cloudy and wet day ahead.'

'My Mum had the best weather forecaster of them all,' recalled Arthur. 'It was a glass jar full of water with a wine bottle turned upside down in it. It was the type of bottle that had a wicker basket round it, and a long neck. When it was going to be fine, the water rose in the bottle; but if it was going to be wet the water dropped back into the jar. When the weather was going to be really bad I have seen a bubble rise out of the bottom of the jar.'

The farm workers, due to close observation of nature all around them, could also make a fair job of forecasting the weather. 'My father's arthritis was always worse in dry weather,' remembered Arthur, who also recalled the following country signs: 'If you are about early in the morning in the harvest time and look at the stubble where the corn has been cut, and it looks like a silver sheen, it is the harvest spider spinning its web across the stubble and the dew is collecting on it, and the early sun catches it so you can see it. You can also see these webs on freshly ploughed fields. This tells you it will be a fine day ahead.'

Another sign of fine weather ahead is a whirlwind. 'We used to call them Jolly Rogers. They usually happened in June or July. I have seen a whole haystack lifted forty to fifty feet into the sky or flung across the yard.

'If you see rabbits feeding late at night, it will be raining next day. "Rain from the east, twenty-four hours at least" is a saying that is rarely wrong.'

Owls don't like wet feathers and won't hunt then, so if they are quiet you can be sure wet weather is on its way. Pheasants have sensitive feet, and often get noisy before thunder arrives. Scarlet pimpernel flowers close up their petals and poplar trees turn up their leaves when it is going to be wet. At night, if the moon has a burr round it means more rain,' explained Arthur. 'If the moon is on its back it will be fine weather but if the moon is up straight it will rain. Rooks circling and flying high indicate windy weather is coming in, but wet weather is to be expected if frogs and toads are seen out of ditches and places around the farm.'

When Arthur was twenty-five, he left the farm in Suffolk. There was a long waiting list for a house on the estate and he planned to get married. He moved to Essex and took up employment doing repair and maintenance of farm machinery. He had done this work on the

Henham Estate. 'Weather didn't matter now I was in engineering full-time, except at harvest time.'

The development of a second Sizewell Plant caused Arthur to move his family to Norfolk in the 1990s. In his retirement he is still aware of the weather. 'The cat washes right behind its ears, not just its face, when it's going to rain and our pug dog has trouble breathing before bad weather arrives. Once the storm is here, breathing is quickly restored to normal, and my daughter's pigmy goats shout to come in at least an hour before the rain arrives.'

Retirement for Arthur is a busy one. He is involved with the Heavy Horse Society, and still enjoys ploughing on local farms. He likes restoring old tractors and vintage machinery, and visits many county rallies demonstrating old tractors, having restored several to their former glory.

Arthur Stockdale driving one of his tractors

Fred Tillet
Farm worker

Fred Tillet was born in 1910 in Hickling, a village that existed long before the Norman Conquest. The Domesday Book (1086) refers to the village as 'Hikelinga'. In 1287 a great flood engulfed the village and 180 people drowned. In 1348 the Black Death struck and more than half the population died. During the Middle Ages peat was dug from the marshes for fuel, the diggings later flooding to form the Broads. Hickling is the largest of the Norfolk Broads and is today famous for its wetland nature reserve. Agriculture has always been a dominant feature of rural life, and farms, carpenters, shoemakers, butchers, reed-cutters, thatchers and blacksmiths thrived around the village. The purpose-built school was opened on January 16th 1861, designed to accommodate 70 children.

Fred and his father in 1923

Fred left school at the age of fourteen, and went to work at Hickling Hall Farm, later moving on to Brumstead Hall Farm. He retired at the age of 65, having daily cycled 12 miles to work. Now, at 89 years, he still cycles to visit friends and family in nearby villages and towns. He says he watches the weather all the time and writes up

111

his forecasts. 'I never got wet through,' said Fred. 'I always got the weather pretty right. I had to watch the wind to set the windmill sails right. I had to watch for icy weather to let water out of the tractors at night. Tractors had five to six gallons of water in them and if it was allowed to freeze it would block the machinery and you would get a cracked cylinder. I didn't like anti-freeze; you couldn't rely on it. If the sky was yellow in the evening it was a sign of rain and wind so you couldn't drill next day so well.'

Fred's parents were not well off, and many a week, they could only afford to buy half a pie at a time. A little poaching greatly enhanced the family diet. On a starlit night with a slight breeze, Fred would go out at midnight and maybe collect four or five rabbits. 'If it was going to be a wet night the rabbits would go out to feed early. You could hear the click of their feet to warn one another of danger.' He would go out fishing also. 'That was best in the early morning,' said Fred, 'that's when the fish were feeding.' If the day was too bright, the catch would be poor, but if it were breezy and cloudy he usually got a good catch. When there was a thick summer fog over the marshes, Fred would say that 'Lantern Jack' was out. He recalls seeing this very clearly over Eastfields in 1917-18 on one of his food forays.

Weather would be turning rough if the animals turned their backs to it, and cows, horses, and sheep would huddle under hedges and fences. If the blackthorn came out early there would be bad weather for a week with cold north-east winds, and if the wind changed direction, a change in the weather always followed.

As Fred ploughed the land with horses, he always noted that if gulls came inland it was a sign of bad weather on the way. Another sign would be that starlings would come on to the reed beds, also crows, 'hedge-hoppers', would come inland and if birds and insects were flying low there was wind and rain approaching with pressure dropping.

Rooks and crows nesting low foretold an unsettled spring, but if they nested high it was taken as a sign of a good summer ahead.

Fred remarked that if there was no dew on the grass, he knew it would be raining by lunchtime. Another sign of rain on the way was a red sky in the morning 'going over to the west, then back again'.

'A sure sign of bad weather on the way was to walk home on a starry night. Clear visibility when you can see a thousand pinpoints of light I never did like!' remarked Fred with a knowing smile.

112

Fred also told me that cows will head to the top of a hill or slope if good weather is on the way, but that sheep get huffy before bad weather. Worms crawling on the top of soil meant that rain can be expected and if they are found on doorsteps, floods should be expected. If swallows leave early, a bad autumn is on its way, and the song of a curlew at dusk is a sure sign of rain.

Horses get restless before rain comes in, stretching out their necks, sniffing the air and turning back their lips. When gulls and crows fly low over the fields and collect 'it's coming rough,' concluded Fred.

Clouds that billow up like big cauliflowers mean that rough weather, even snow, may be expected, and when cattle stand with their backs to the wind, rain is on the way. Flies bite more readily when rain is on the way also.

Fred told me that he also could 'smell the rain' before it arrived. 'The explanation for this could be that flowers and plants give off more scent when the air is moist,' he mused.

'A summer fog will roast a dog, but a winter fog will freeze a hog,' quoted Fred, who also remembered that in his youth fogs seem to 'hang over the fields' much more persistently than they do in present times.

Rain falling ahead of a strengthening wind indicated stormy weather on its way, but wind ahead of rain meant that the wind will die as the rain arrived, concluded Fred, who then recalled that if he saw long glistening strands of cobwebs it indicated a spell of settled weather ahead.

When frogspawn appeared earlier than usual Fred expected a good spring; if the spawn was in the middle of the pond it indicated a dry spell, but if the spawn were laid around the edges of the water, cold wet windy spring weather was likely.

Fred told me that when he heard countryside noises especially clearly, even footsteps and voices a long way off, he knew rain would arrive within twenty-four hours, and when farm birds, especially geese and ducks, used to preen fanatically, he knew they were getting their feathers in order before the wet weather arrived.

John King

Head Gamekeeper, Holkham Estate

John was born in North Norfolk and went to the local village school, leaving at fifteen years. 'I had no ambitions there,' he said. 'All I ever wanted to do was to be a gamekeeper.' His father put him into the Hill and Osborne agricultural engineering firm based in Burnham Market, but after hearing the boy crying himself to sleep every night, he allowed him to leave and work on a farm. There he helped the gamekeeper, and had his own gun. 'I had no brothers or sisters, but my gun and dog replaced them,' was his frank comment. The boy had a natural ability, 'had an eye', and when the gamekeeper died of a heart attack on shoot day, John replaced him, staying there 'man and boy' until he married. He moved next to Thornham and worked there eight years as gamekeeper with one retired beat keeper. The post of head gamekeeper at Holkham Hall Estate fell vacant, and Lord Leicester, after interviewing John, offered him the job.

Now John had eight men working for him, with twenty-five thousand acres, twenty-five tenant farmers, a deer herd of over eight hundred animals and their annual cull, the shoots, and the letting of day-shoots, all to be responsible for. In addition to being deer manager, for over forty years, as a hobby and business, he ran sixty hives of bees, and pronounced bees the best weather forecasters he had ever come across.

Now, after keepering for forty-five years, he goes out with his dogs four to five days a week, 'picking up' and loading, also working as a part-time pest-control officer for English Nature. During the summer, John works at the local holiday camp on their 'pitch & putt' green. One of John's boys seemed to have inherited his father's eye, because he has become an international bowls player, and when not travelling the world taking part in competitions, he works in pest-control in Norfolk. Another of John's sons is a fisherman, who keeps his boat in Wells harbour and also serves on the Wells lifeboat.

When keepering, John automatically listened to the television and radio forecasts, considered the weather maps, then made up his own forecasts, using his local knowledge. 'I could often produce a better forecast than they did,' he said. 'They [the professionals] would assume the fronts were going from west to east, but I could also take into account the local features. In North Norfolk we have very strong geographical considerations. Sometimes I would listen to their predictions for a thunderstorm, but I knew that if the tide was in, the storm would come in and split on the river Ouse at King's Lynn, half going up into Lincolnshire, with the remainder coming round by Hunstanton and then out into the Wash. Hunstanton often gets the rain, whilst lower down in the county it remains dry.'

John said that when planning a day's shoot, he had to know the probable movements of fronts coming through the area. 'Birds, particularly the grey partridge, don't like flying with the wind with it coming up their backsides; they prefer to fly at an angle to the wind.' He would have plan A and B when deciding on the day's shoot, and Lord Leicester would be involved in the plans of where to place the guns according to the wind direction. 'Some drives you simply can't take if the wind direction changes,' John said. 'Some birds like to slide the wind and won't fly into a strong wind.'

'You can tell by the feel of the wind if rain is on the way. You just feel the moisture in the air. The local Anglia weather forecast predicted rain a couple of days ago, but it never came in - there was too much wind. I could see there were two layers of clouds; the low cloud came fast but the thicker high clouds hung about, and you don't get the weight of rain in those low clouds that you do out of the thicker higher clouds.'

The subject of rain was next discussed. John said 'You have to know when to shut the birds up when you are rearing pheasants, and when it is safe to leave them out. You get to read the skies. I can read a Norfolk sky quite well, but I'd be lost when forecasting the weather in other parts of the country. I don't know the names of the clouds, but the stretchy grey clouds, not the fluffy white ones, usually forecast watery weather. If the sun shines through the clouds, but the old sun looks watery, you can expect rain that day. If you look out in the morning and see a red sky, with the sun coming up, then dropping back, you can be certain wet weather is on the way, but if the sun comes up and goes right over, good weather is on its way. A pink morning sky usually means that wind is on its way, but when high altitude clouds stream above lower clouds which are slower moving, it is likely pressure is dropping and wind and rain are on the way. When the wind comes in from the west, rain is on its way often, but winds from the east are drying winds and colder ones. When easterly winds are established, these "lazy" winds usually bring in severe frosts.' John said that years ago one could expect many weeks of hard wind-frosts when the spring easterly winds set in, but in recent years this predictable pattern was missing.

I asked John about colours in the sky in relation to weather forecasting, and he replied that a dark green or a sharp green sky indicated a spell of frosty evenings. Haloes round the moon were also a weather indicator. 'Burr close rain soon, burr far rain far', and the intensity of the yellow halo also indicated the intensity of the rain pattern. 'Colour indicators in the sky alter according to the size of the moon,' said John. 'When the moon is on the make you get sharper features in the sky.' Then he quoted, 'When the moon is on the right it's alright, and when the moon is on the left that's all that's left. When the sun goes down bright and clear usually the next day will be fair,' he continued, and said, 'You don't know what you do know, because you're living with the weather and unconsciously are always assessing it.' But he always sensed a good weather spell because everything was happy and relaxed and life was easy. 'Nothing is better than a happy dawn chorus.'

John has often given local talks on 'The Life of a Gamekeeper'. 'February 2nd the year starts', then he would describe the four seasons. But he said, 'We don't get the four seasons like we used to; the weather has changed so much in the last few years, but we are still getting the signs.'

John has always seen his job as keeping a balance with nature; man, the dominant animal, has a responsibility to keep an even balance, controlling vermin such as rats, moles, carrion crows, magpies, jays and, more recently, foxes. As a gamekeeper he enjoys most the wild bird shoots. 'I don't like to see big bags of, say, five hundred birds taken in a day. I prefer to see, say, two hundred good quality wild birds, pheasants and partridges, in the bag.' When at Thornham, he had to breed to kill, but enjoyed much more the wildlife shoots rather than the reared bird shoots.

Finally John talked about animals as a rough indicator of weather. He said he always had to move his sixty hives of bees at night, and always more than a distance of three or four miles, otherwise the worker bees would return and sit on the floor where their hives used to be. His practice was to take the hives to fields of oilseed rape in the summer and then, in the early spring, place them in fruit tree orchards. If the weather was going to set in cold and wet the bees would make an early return to their hive, but when there was a good, settled spell, they would be out working very early and stay out all day. 'Bees will slide the wind,' said John, 'they don't like flying into it. They are the best weather indicators I know.' If wet weather was on the way, they would be out doing their housework, clearing out the debris from the hive and tidying up.

John told me that if rough weather was on the way, cattle would huddle together in the fields and 'heap up' and face into the coming weather, whereas horses would make for the sheltered end of the field to get out of the wind, long before it arrived. Pheasants would go up to roost if bad weather was coming, because they wanted to keep their feathers dry, but when the climate was warm and settled they would 'jug down' on the floor. Rabbits would come out to feed late if the evening was fair but if rain was expected they would come out to feed early, or not come out at all. Hares do not go to ground in wet weather but keep on the move and feed by night, lying down in 'forms' or shallow depressions on the ground. They would run about more in rainy weather, not liking to lie upon damp soil, and would always face rain and wind, and when it was wet, go to high ground, where the drainage of the land would be better.

As John finished his mardle on the weather, it seemed completely natural that his next job was to take his grandson out with the dogs.

Concluding Thoughts

Being a keen sailor and gardener, my interest in weather goes back a long way. Norfolk-born, the countryside and coastline are also of great concern to me. Living amongst local fishermen and land workers served to deepen my care and concern for these issues.

Recently I attended a course at Cambridge University called 'Weather, Climate and Ecosystems'. Apart from learning a great deal about the possible causes and effects of global warming, and likely changes in the future course of the Gulf Stream. I was delighted to realize that my respect for my Norfolk friends was deepened, even more because their exceptional observation gave detailed and accurate weather information relating to the area where they lived and worked. Even the professional forecasters with access to a wealth of meteorological instruments could hardly be more accurate, because they did not have knowledge of local features, like hot spots, which may delay or divert a carefully-worked-out weather trend.

For example, Shrimp Davies was quite sure that 'weather headings' indicated that stormy weather was on its way. 'Little squares of light that have all the colours of the rainbow in them' was how Shrimp described them.

During my Cambridge course I learnt that this optical effect was the result of reflection and refraction of light by hexagonal ice crystals in the atmosphere. Shrimp was also very definite that 'sun dawgs' meant bad weather was on its way. On my course I read that sun dogs or 'mock suns' are the result of sunlight passing through a layer of ice crystals, whether contained within cirrus clouds, or falling at lower levels, and that they can only be seen when the hexagonal ice crystals are oriented horizontally - that is, with the flat sides facing down. Cirrus clouds also indicate deteriorating weather conditions. Shrimp, who left school at twelve years old as top scholar, could hardly have been taught that cirrus clouds are found above 7,000 metres indicating strong winds in the upper troposphere, which often herald an approaching warm front. However his apprenticeship with his uncle, and sharp observational skills, taught him that wispy white filaments in the sky nicknamed 'mares' tails' foretold bad weather, and also that seeing sun dogs and weather headings were important things to consider when deciding whether or not to launch and go to their gear miles offshore.

The Cambridge course also highlighted for me the link between weather lore and actual weather. For example -

'Robins singing high - fine and dry;
Robins singing low - too wet to mow.'

Robins are very territorial and need song posts to proclaim their patch. Rain is on its way when they sing on low branches with their tails down, but fine weather is assured if the robins sing high up in hedges, and their tails are up.

The male mistle thrush is one of the few birds that sing when thunderstorms are approaching - hence its name 'storm cock'. Green woodpeckers, known as rain birds, are reputed to use a laughing call when rain is due. High-flying swifts and swallows flying low foretell wet weather on its way, because they are feeding on insects that stay close to plant cover when damp weather is felt.

As John King noted, bees have an impressive reputation for sensing weather trends. Beekeepers try to keep away from hives before thunderstorms because they believe bees to be bad-tempered, being sensitive, not only to warmth and light, but also to electricity in the atmosphere.

'When bees crowd out of their hive
The weather makes it good to be alive.
When bees crowd into the hive again
It's a sure sign of storms and rain.'

Another country saying, 'Rain before seven, clear by eleven', may be relatively accurate since it takes a weather front about five hours to pass from west to east across the country.

'When you see gossamer flying, be sure the air is drying' points to the fact that spiders won't spin in humid conditions, and usually assume a rainfall position, hanging straight down from their webs with front legs stretched out below, to act as guttering to drain water off the webs.

'When the ditch and pond offend the nose
Look for rain and stormy blows.'

This saying relates to atmospheric pressure falling as rain is approaching, which triggers the release of fungal spores in the soil. Their smell is often picked up by people with a good sense of smell. In the 1950s Australian chemists traced these smells down to the soil.

Red sky at morning, shepherd's warning' makes sense when one realises that a red glow in the western sky in the morning is a sign of approaching wet weather, because the sun is reflecting on to the incoming clouds of a 'low'.

As the world's weather warms, wildlife and plants will respond. Already Mediterranean plants and animals are migrating into southern England - not only birds, butterflies and animals, but also unwanted species like mosquitoes. Fish also are altering their sea movements.

Scientists are busy noting these rapid changes in our environment, and no doubt those that work on the land and the sea will be in the forefront seeing how humans must adapt to survive our changing climate.

Dr Jenner, an 18th-century physician, was asked by his lady friend if he thought it would rain tomorrow as she was planning to take him on a picnic. His reply encapsulates many weather sayings and old wives' tales.

'Hark! How the chairs and tables crack,
Old Betty's joints are on the rack;
Loud quack the ducks, the peacocks cry,
The distant hills are seeming nigh.

How restless are the snorting swine,
The busy flies disturb the kine!
Low o'er the grass the swallow wings,
The cricket too, how he sings!
Puss on the hearth, with velvet paws
Sits smoothing o'er her whiskered jaws.

Through the clear streams the fishes rise,
And nimbly catch the incautious flies;
And sheep were seen at early light,
Cropping the meads with eager bite.

Through June, the air is cold and chill,
The mellow blackbird's voice is still.
The glow-worms, numerous and bright,
Illum'ed the dewy dell last night.
At dusk the squalid toad was seen,
Hopping and crawling o'er the green.

120

The frog has lost his yellow vest,
And in a dingy suit is dressed.
The leech, disturbed is newly risen,
Quite to the summit of his prison.
The whirling winds the dust obeys,
And in her rapid eddy plays;
My dog so altered in his taste,
Quits mutton bones on grass to feast;
And, see you - rooks how odd their flight,
They imitate the gliding kite;
Or seem to precipitate to fall,
As if they felt the piercing ball.

The hollow winds begin to blow,
The clouds look black, the glass is low;
The soot falls down, the spaniels sleep,
The spiders from their cobwebs peep.

Last night the sun went pale to bed,
The moon in haloes hide her head.
The working shepherd heaves a sigh,
For see! a rainbow spans the sky.
The walls are damp, the ditches smell.
Closed is the scarlet pimpernel.

'Twill surely rain. I see with sorrow,
Our jaunt must be put off tomorrow.'

Appendix 1. Global Warming - Global Warning! by Pat Gowen

(Abridged)

There must be many who after the torrential rain of this past winter are saying 'What's all this about droughts, a Mediterranean climate and more sunshine then?'

Odd that it may seem, the experience of severe flooding, saturated ground and increased landslip that we have experienced this past year is due to Global Warming, or the 'Greenhouse effect' as we commonly term it. The increased temperatures over land and sea are dictating increased evaporation, this leading to drought, crop failure, increasing forest fires and greenery die-back in the hotter areas. The warm moisture-laden air then migrates to the cooler areas and precipitates, producing the deluges that we are now experiencing. The higher latitudes see more winter rain, but also see far less of it during the summer growing season. Not a good mixture!

We are losing our temperate climate to become more like southern Europe and North Africa. In summers we shall suffer droughts and grave water shortages for public supply, agriculture and the environment. In spring and autumn we shall see rapid changes of weather with more equinoctial gales, tornados and other unseasonable manifestations. In the winters we shall experience deeper and more frequent barometric lows and more rain, thus more flooding and land saturation, hence a threat to housing, life and livelihood and food production. We are already experiencing far stronger northerly winds that last longer, resulting in escalating erosion of our shoreline, loss of coastal dwellings and farms, footpaths, salt marshes and wildlife habitats. The future will produce greater and more frequent North Sea surges.

But what we are seeing in Britain is nothing to the hazard threatened to other parts of the world. The floods seen in Africa, Asia, America and Australia have been far worse, drowning and dispossessing millions of people. The droughts that they have experienced have killed many from starvation, whilst huge forest fires produced by the dehydration have raged through all continents including Europe and America, destroying lives, livelihoods and homes.

Whole islands in the Pacific and Indian Oceans will be submerged by the rising sea levels brought about by marine thermal expansion added to by the melting of polar icecaps and glaciers.

Many of the world's major cities, New York, Rio de Janeiro and London, to name but a few, will be inundated, whilst here in East Anglia we shall lose many of our coastal towns and low-lying inland areas. Cambridge and Ely will need the suffix 'on sea' added to their titles, if not 'under sea'. Some scientists see signs that the Gulf Stream, like El Nino, is beginning to fail due to the lowering south-to-north differential. If we lose this, Britain will lose its temperate climate to experience the same winter temperatures as other regions of the same latitude, e.g. northern Canada and Siberia, where -45C is the winter norm. That's hard to equate with 'Earth Warming', but it is already beginning to happen!

The basic problem is fossil fuel burning causing ever-increasing emissions of

122

CO_2. Every time we use that car we add to it directly by burning petrol or diesel fuel. Every time we turn the heat up one degree, leave that light on or heat up that extra water, we add to it indirectly. Each time we leave our doors and windows open we lose heat that needs to be regenerated. We are also losing it if we have no adequate roof, floor and wall insulation. On top of this we can use low energy light bulbs. Attending to these points will not only save you at least 30% of your energy bills but help to save the environment too.

Methane is another 'greenhouse gas', twenty times more damaging than CO_2. The poor recycling record of the UK, Norfolk in particular, means that thousands of tons of excess packaging are rotting away on landfill tips generating huge levels of methane, little of which is recycled for fuel. Our government is spending only £120m per annum on recycling but £380m on incineration, which latter will serve to release even more heat and CO_2.

Recognising some of these causes threatening the continuity to life on earth the world's nations met in Japan to form the Kyoto Protocol committing all of this planet's nations to a cut in CO_2 emissions. All governments except the United States agreed whilst Japan and Australia were far from enthusiastic.

The United States has the highest per capita CO_2 emissions by far. They have 4% of the world's population, but are responsible for 25% of the world's greenhouse gases. They promised a cut of 7% of the 1990 levels over the following ten years, which is nowhere near enough, as a 65% cut in emissions is vital to achieve the balance. In practice, the USA increased CO_2 output by more than 10% in the same period!

Soon after obtaining the Presidency, Mr Bush announced that he would renege completely on the United Nations Kyoto agreement, so forfeiting the future of the planet to the dictates of the powerful Texan oil interests that funded his election campaign.

In the last analysis, with our 'responsible' authorities failing to take the measures so vital to the continuity of life on this planet, it seems to come down to we people who actually generate the problems on an individual and collective basis. In addition to measures suggested above, we could refuse to purchase multi-packaged consumer products. In the absence of a countywide recycling scheme, we can perform this on an individual basis by composting our garden refuse, paper and cardboard. We can use the sun and air to dry our washing instead of that tumble dryer, and take our own bags to the shop instead of using new ones each time.

Appendix 2. Our Disappearing Coastline by Pat Gowen
(Extracts)

History

For many centuries now the East Anglian coastline has been gently eroding for natural reasons. Apart from the effects of the onslaught of major storms and surges, there has been a slow and steady but nevertheless relentless regression. In the short term the high beach sand loss resulting from the strong onshore north winds of the winter months are normally balanced by reinstatement during the summer months when the prevailing offshore south to south-west winds occur.

Natural Sinkage

Eurasian tectonic base plate stretching from the North American continent is causing Scotland to rise slowly from the sea, with the resulting tip effect causing south-east England to sink. Although this rate was as much as 3 millimetres per year in the past, it is now judged to be in the region of 1.5 mm per annum and still reducing. Kent, Essex, Suffolk and Norfolk plus part of Lincolnshire are very slowly sinking. Man does not have the technological ability to tackle this natural threat.

Global Warming & Rising Sea Levels

Since the industrial revolution of the nineteenth century, earth warming has played its role in bringing about the encroachment of the sea. Ever increasing carbon dioxide emissions from power stations, industry and traffic have resulted in rising sea levels. Polar ice cap and glacial melting is now adding over two millimetres per year, and this melt rate is increasing. Due to Global Warming, sea expansion is giving an additional sea level rise of up to seven millimetres per annum; this too is increasing. All of these factors add to the inland progression of the North Sea. Until governments fully recognise Global Warming and the Greenhouse Effect and take action on the fossil fuel carbon dioxide emissions that are the main cause, no relief is possible, and regression impossible. Yet, the rapid increase of erosion of England's eastern seaboard evidenced over the past twenty years is far greater than can be ascribed to the above factors. There is now strong supportive correlated evidence that offshore dredging is playing the major role in the loss of our coastal fringe.

Seabed Exploitation

Licensed by the Department of the Environment, eight different companies are currently operating 2,000- to 8,000-ton dredgers on our offshore sand banks. They extract the sand and gravel as a highly profitable commercial enterprise, sucking up all the base sediment and the life forms they support, returning the unprofitable choking silt back to the sea. Not only does this exploitation create a marine desert devoid of all sea life in the dredged area, it also smothers a further vast area of living seabed many miles down tide.

The Home Market

The demand for sand, shingle and gravel for the construction industry is enormous in the United Kingdom, amounting to 5.5 metric tonnes of aggregate per person per year. Most of this requirement now comes from the sea and well over 30% of this from the East Anglian coastline. Dredged sand was used to construct the huge Sizewell nuclear power stations. Much of it is used for housing and the government's roads programme. 200,000 tons is required for every mile of constructed motorway.

The Export Market

Most of the dredged aggregate is exported. Britain is the second largest producer of marine-dredged construction aggregates in the world. Just over half the sand taken is sold to Holland, a huge cargo boatful going to Nieuport every day. Even back in 1955 over half of the dredged material was landed at Amsterdam and Flushing, more than at any British port. The Netherlands is a ready profitable market with a constant requirement, but Holland 'buys British' because it strictly prohibits aggregate dredging off its own coastline due to the erosion that would result were it permitted. In the Netherlands much of the aggregate is used to build up the Dutch sea defences, a considerate defensive strategy that many people of the East Anglian coastline region regard with envy.

Offshore Dredging Levels

Open cast seabed mining for aggregate commenced in 1973 when just 3 million metric tonnes were removed. By 1992 the annual rate had risen to 18 million tons. In 1994 22 million metric tonnes were taken. As over 80% of the sand extracted at the dredging site is in the form of non-required fine silt, this is washed back into the sea. This silt then smothers the seabed for up to five miles down tide, so destroying the marine seabed environment of an even greater area.

Offshore Gas Extraction

Seabed subsidence brought about by gas and oil extraction is another factor causing erosion. The link between the sinkage of the ocean floor and coastal erosion has already been proven on the coastline of the Waddensea. The need to prop and raise the interlinked UK offshore gas rigs off the Norfolk coastline due to base subsidence shows that it is happening here too.

Coastline Property Losses

In the past ten years the level of sea bottom sediment exploitation has increased enormously. Consequently major destruction of livelihood and property has resulted along the North Sea coast from Humberside down to Essex. Due to sand and dune erosion, the mean high and low tide marks have advanced by over one hundred metres along many undefended parts of the north-east Norfolk coast. At many points between Walcott and Caister-on-Sea over seven metres' depth of beach sand has been stripped from the popular holiday beaches.

Many have become inaccessible due to the steep verticals created by dune undermining and the destruction of access paths. Beach slopes have increased, and stones or muddy marl now predominate where once there were golden sands. This causes a major loss of amenity and a consequent loss in value to income from the tourist trade, which has decreased to less than one third of its former capture in the past ten-year period. South of the Humber Estuary farmhouses and farmland are being lost to the sea at a frightening rate. In north Norfolk both Trimingham and

A well-shaft at Happisburgh, once well inland, and now left standing while the land around it has been washed away by the sea

Overstrand have lost their coast roads. At Overstrand many valuable homes have tumbled to the sea as the cliff below them has been gnawed away. The third of a series of retreating sea defences at Happisburgh has failed, and the cliff is rapidly eroding back toward the village. The coast road and the houses beside it have been lost to the sea. No real defences are planned as the money required, too much for North Norfolk Council, is not forthcoming from central government. The once sandy 100-metre-long beach at Sea Palling was reduced to a thin strip of sticky clay marl seen only at low tide, as the sea came right up to the sea wall now, each high tide undermining the sea wall. But at least the highly expensive offshore rock reef scheme has worked so far, although its sand capture has denied the needed sedimentary sand deposits for the coastline to the south-east. A 150-metres retreat of sand and dunes has resulted at Waxham and Winterton-on-Sea.

The Threat to Coastal Wildlife

Beach destruction just south of Winterton-on-Sea has brought about the loss of the Little Tern shore colony, whilst the soft cliff nesting-hole destruction has decimated the sand martins. The previous dune habitat of nightjars and skylarks plus much of the earlier glory of the flora, grasses and dune topography from the Great Winterton Valley SSSI up to Sea Palling has been destroyed. The previous common seal colony has been lost between Waxham and Winterton. Holme, a most important nature reserve, is now receding rapidly; thirty-nine per cent of the north Norfolk salt marshes have already been lost to the sea. RAMSAR sites, which by a treaty the UK

126

is deemed to protect, maintain, or if damaged, restore or replace are now part of 'managed retreat', e.g. an 'allow it to go' approach. The Cley and Salthouse bird reserve (a RAMSAR site) is to have its present shingle protection bank abandoned and a new bank created some 100m inland. This bank has been stable and effective since it was built in the mid-1600's, but since offshore dredging commenced has been depleted by over 60%. The impact to the creatures of the seabed and the species dependent upon this has been enormous, as long evidenced by the inshore fishermen of the East Anglian coast.

The Threat to Marine Life

The 'Seas at Risk' Group headed by Roger Lankester fears that the deep holes made in the seabed sediment may be causing an imbalance in the sea. Nutrient release was discovered following deep bait-digging over wide areas, when the sludge and phosphates deposited by untreated marine sewage outfalls were freed. The impact of dredging is far greater than this. Nutrient imbalance is known to be the main cause of algal blooms, which when toxic can bring about the shellfish bans and so do further damage to the marine environment and the fishing industry. To add to this, Britain is the only country in Europe still pumping and dumping untreated sewage and sludge to the marine environment, both major nutrient contributors, despite the demands of the North Sea Conference, MARPOL and EC Directives.

The Threat to Shellfish and Birdlife

The release of the fine sediment by the dredgers is known by the fishermen to be one of the main causes of the serious loss of cockles, mussels and other shellfish and shrimp around the areas being dredged near The Wash. Since dredging began, the stocks have lowered annually. The RSPB is concerned about the loss of oystercatchers and other important wading birds, which have reduced by up to 70% in the past few years. Shellfish food supply loss is believed responsible for the serious decline.

Coastal Homes Destruction

At Hemsby over 100 metres of beach width and dune frontage as well as seven metres' beach sand depth disappeared since offshore dredging commenced. Where once since living memory a quadruple dune system was stable between the sea and the great Winterton Valley SSSI, now only one third of the last surviving dune remains. The Valley floor is barely above the mean tidemark, and slopes downhill to the sub-sea level Brograve levels. A winter surge may soon erode the last remaining dune to bring about marine inundation of north Martham, Potter Heigham, Hickling and the entire Broads system. Eighty-nine coastal bungalow homes have been destroyed at Hemsby by erosion of their previously stable dune base in just a half-mile stretch of coastline north of Hemsby Gap. Where from 1932 to 1984 they stood 60 metres back from the highest tide mark is now sea. The Hemsby lifeboat shed, built at Hemsby Gap well back from the ocean just seven years ago, has had to be replaced by another further inland. The original is soon to be taken by the sea despite the earnest endeavours by the crew to save it. Owners receive no compensation for loss, are unable to insure, and even have to meet the costs of final demolition and removal of their destroyed properties.

Beach Losses, threats...and gains!

Many unexploded mines, wartime bombs, mortar bombs and shells once covered by deep sand are now being regularly exposed on our beaches as the covering sand has been stripped. At Waxham, the long-sunken wartime landing-craft defence system was uncovered by sand erosion leaving a series of sharp steel spikes. This new hazard impaled two paddlers, one swimmer and one boat in the 1996 holiday season. On the beach between Hemsby Gap and California the Coastguard almost lost his life when his Range Rover sank up to its windows in the sand-stripped soft marl. Only two years ago this stretch of sand was four metres deep and extended 100 metres. Now each high tide takes more beach sand cover and laps the soft sand cliff, eating its way relentlessly towards California village.

The erosion has had its good points at California, as a cache of gold and silver coins dating from Celtic times was found in immaculate condition, having been buried deeply for many centuries.